borderline

Keith Adamson, *Mother Nature's Son*, first published by Third House in *The Freezer Counter*, reproduced by permission of the author.

Bill Douglas, from *My Way Home* (adapted from Douglas's original film script), first published in *Bill Douglas: A Lanternist's Account*. The films comprising *The Bill Douglas Trilogy* were produced by BFI Production. Reproduced by kind permission of Peter Jewell (the Bill Douglas Estate).

Carol Ann Duffy, 'Mrs Darwin', from *The World's Wife*. Reproduced by kind permission of Picador, MacMillan, London, UK.

Janice Galloway, *bisex*, extract from *Where You Find It*, published by Jonathan Cape. Reproduced by permission of The Random House Group Ltd.

Alasdair Gray, *One for the Album*, extract from *Something Leather*, published by Jonathan Cape. Reproduced by permission of The Random House Group Ltd.

Thomas Healy, extract from *Rolling*, published by Polygon. Reproduced by kind permission of the author.

Jackie Kay, extract from *Trumpet*. Reproduced by kind permission of Picador, MacMillan, London, UK.

James Kelman, *Pictures*, extract from a collection called *The Burn*, published by Secker and Warburg. Reproduced by permission of The Random House Group Ltd.

A.L. Kennedy, extract from *Everything You Need*, published by Jonathan Cape. Reproduced by permission of The Random House Group Ltd.

Gordon Legge, extracts from *I Love Me (Who Do You Love?)*. Reproduced by kind permission of Polygon.

Jimmy McGovern, extract from *Priest*. Reproduced by kind permission of The Agency (London) Ltd, *Priest* © 1995 by Jimmy McGovern.

Edwin Morgan, extract from his biography, first published in *Footsteps and Witnesses*, edited by Bob Cant. Reproduced by kind permission of the author. 'Christmas Eve' taken from *Collected Poems* Paperback Ed. 1996. Reproduced by kind permission of Carcanet Press Ltd.

Manda Scott, extract from *Stronger Than Death*, first published by Headline Book Publishing plc. Reproduced by kind permission of Hodder Headline Ltd.

Ali Smith, *Free Love*, from *Free Love*. Reproduced by kind permission of Virago Press.

Alexander Trocchi, extracts from *Cain's Book*. Reproduced by kind permission of The Calder Educational Trust.

Irvine Welsh, extract from *Marabou Stork Nightmares*, published by Jonathan Cape. Reproduced by kind permission of The Random House Group Ltd.

Graham Woolaston, extract from *The Learning of Paul O'Neill*, published by Millivres Books, Brighton, 1995. Used with permission of the publisher.

borderline

the mainstream book of scottish gay writing

introduction by Toni Davidson

edited by joseph mills

MAINSTREAM
PUBLISHING

EDINBURGH AND LONDON

First published in Great Britain in 2001 by
MAINSTREAM PUBLISHING COMPANY (EDINBURGH) LTD
7 Albany Street
Edinburgh EH1 3UG

ISBN 1 84018 507 4

A catalogue record for this book is available from the British Library

Typeset in Berkeley
Printed and bound in Great Britain by
Creative Print and Design Wales

'You can stay if you like
If you want you can call it home'
Bill Douglas, from *My Way Home*

'There's more to love than boy meets girl'
Jimmy Somerville

This is dedicated to

Peter Burton

For invaluable practical help with editing an anthology and for letting me do those four-page, full-colour, glossy-pictured articles in *Gay Times* in the early '90s, eulogising Marky Mark et al. Those were the days . . . and for publishing more Scottish gay writers than most Scottish publishers

and

Keith Adamson, Sebastian Beaumont, Jack Dickson, Thomas Healy, Richard Smith, Graeme Woolaston, Jennifer, Kari, Muna, Palma.

contents

introduction
TONI DAVIDSON
TONI DAVIDSON

Back in the now strangely halcyon days of Glasgow's Mayfest, I organised a series of Lesbian and Gay Literary events. These workshops and readings were ambitious in nature but I was optimistic that I would find both willing participants and an eager audience. One event even caused – where would a festival be without it – a little controversy. I had asked James Kelman, Alasdair Gray and Janice Galloway to come and read something that they felt was appropriate to such an event. All three accepted and read from work which was relevant and entertaining. There had been misgivings however – one gay academic said that these writers had no place at a lesbian and gay event.

All my writing life I have come across this sort of reaction. If I am gay then I will write gay-related fiction to be published by a gay publisher for a gay audience. This was the way of things when I emerged both as a writer and as gay in the early '80s. But I didn't like it. Sure, there are several of my stories which have predominantly gay themes and have been used by gay publishing houses but when I began to veer away from this niche, when there was nothing gay about something I had written, it would no longer be of interest. Great. I was gay and a writer but unless I was writing about gay-specific themes (whatever they are) no one was interested.

The French writer Yves Navarre was invited to a Lesbian and Gay Writing event in the late '80s and he turned down the invitation by saying, 'I am gay, I am a writer, I am not a gay writer.' I wouldn't call this a mantra that I lived by but I did find it reassuring. Even before I had a readership I knew that I didn't want to write for a specific audience, I didn't want to queer my prose and limit my themes and language. I was wary of being stuck in a pigeonhole that I couldn't get out of. That wasn't and isn't why I write. Labels are media and whether it's ScotLit or GayLit you have to kick against the pricks that seek to restrict.

I guess a lot has changed. Quite a few of the gay publishers have gone and most of the niche bookshops have disappeared. There are still quite a few gay writing groups and at this entry level to the writing world much good can come from the support and mutual criticism of fellow writers but the literary world that awaits them is an assimilated one – or so it likes to think. Many gay writers writing sexuality-specific prose and poetry have been picked up by mainstream publishing houses, without any discernible compromise in content or attitude. And this was a worry. A few decades ago The Violet quill club in New York sought to bring together a group of writers including Edmund White who were exasperated that they were either being ignored by mainstream publishing houses or being asked to change unacceptable descriptions. This is of course intolerable and if such times were revisited then I would be the first to jump back into the ghetto but we can take comfort from the fact that 'out there' gay writers like Dennis Cooper and P.P. Hartnott can be published successfully while retaining their provocative and decidedly left-field voice.

Mainstream's publication of Joseph Mills's anthology is a timely one. Here we have some wonderful writing by a wide range of writers, extracted and commissioned to create a determinedly broad picture of Scottish writing. There are gay characters, perspectives, themes and – or maybe that should be 'but' – there is a whole lot more. *Borderline* celebrates the diverse and unniched exploration of all things gay. I have no idea what these writers do in bed but knowing writers I am sure it's better not to ask.

section 28

EDWIN MORGAN

EDWIN MORGAN

God said to Winning: 'You are not.
Winning, I mean. You and your lot
Are rowing backward this time round.
You are unsound, my mannie, unsound.
Your favourite sound-bite, gay perversion,
Is not in my New Authorised Version.
I think you ought to buy a copy:
Squeeze it out of Souter's poppy.
I may not keep a place for you
To sup your heavenly honeydew.
What can you learn from my abjuring?
The last seat went to Alan Turing.'

January 2000

JANICE GALLOWAY

bisex

I worry.
Sometimes I need to hear your voice.

I worry. I phone.
You are often out when I phone.

I walk to the far end of the kitchen and hold the kettle under the tap, watch the red marker on the side rise on the fresh water. You could be shopping but not this late: a concert maybe, a show. Walking somewhere, back streets under the streetlamps, the park no one would go to the park at night, the middle of the town. I have no way of knowing. The pictures then, the sauna trying not to think the sauna. The kettle is half full. Four cups. The Sauna. I switch the tap off with one hand, bracing the muscles in the other for the weight of carrying, turn away from my reflection in the window, the rictus of polished jars behind the sink.

Three bags left. Three white purses pooling brown dust. That means six cups of tea if I'm careful. Six for one. I replace the blue and white lid so I don't have to think about there being less now and dowse the first square, fighting it back under with the stream of boiling water every time it tries to surface, than coax it with the spoon before fishing it into another cup for later. I'm running out of milk. Just enough so the tea turns cloudy auburn, seeping from the unmixed splash of white. Greyish white. The kitchen table, the hot cylinder between my hands. The sauna a disco or pub a pub always the same ones. Always. The same ones. Eyes closed, rubbing my mouth against the cup. Even when it burns I don't pull away.

You
You reach across the table.

There is a glass with a slice of lemon, bubbles gathering like spawn along the rim. Your hand lays stripes on the frosted bowl. Your hand. It lifts the glass, settles it against your mouth momentarily, puts it back in exactly the same place. Holding a glass for no reason is what I do, not you. It's near an ashtray, stubbed with butts. Your hair is only just too long, blond creeper over the collar of your jacket at the back. At the front it makes spikes in your eyes. Between that and the smoke in here you can hardly see. Hair in your eyes, booze and no specs not even any sign of the specs. Little vanities leave you wide open. Regardless, you lift the glass again, sip. The way you swallow, jerk the plumb line of that maleness in your throat is smooth, practiced. The way you settle the glass back, running your finger and thumb the length of its stem, watching it fizz.

My stomach dips.

Someone is pulling into focus behind the crook of your arm where it lifts, fetches a cigarette to your mouth. The arm stays flexed, waiting for someone to offer a match. I can't tell if you know he is there, whether you move knowing you are observed or not. In any case, he approaches while you strike and pout, inching the cigarette for the flame the way I've seen you do it a hundred times, eyes puckering up when you draw and his hand touches the table. Your table. You peer at the nameless hand, flicking your head to clear your vision, inhaling, blowing the match out with the first breath of smoke. And you let him sit. You raise your eyes slowly, blowing the match dead. You always let him sit.

And I don't know. I don't know how you begin with these men.

After the shared silences, the contact that implies nothing and everything, messages that could be retracted as soon as understood, after you approach each other, how the real game starts. How you admit to each other what you are doing, whether there is no need. Euphemism and hedging, daring to meet his eyes for whole seconds, tipping your tongue against your carefully white teeth. You play games you would not begin to play with me, risking everything and nothing, waiting for a sign. And sooner or later it comes, though neither of you will be able to say afterwards when that moment was or how it was reached. A change in the temperature of the shared glances, maybe. Or he could simply say it out loud. I don't know. I don't know how it is decided, the rising to leave together, how you choose: whether tonight it's you or him who stands up first. Whether you have somewhere to go, whether you wait while he finishes a drink and wipes his mouth or whether you leave and he follows. His strange scent tracking you down, maybe knowing somewhere warm and safe. Whether it is only the bus shelter or back street, opened coats and the press of concrete at your back. Whether you touch first or he does. I wonder and try not to think, thinking anyway. Either way, there are always folds of cloth. I always see folds of cloth.

Your hand stretching across the drapery of his jeans to his belt, your fingers lifting the buckle to slip the leather. Blond fingers, taut with muscle, white as mushroom stalks, free the buckle and find the zip, a single nail running the length of closed teeth towards the tag to inch it down. Your lips part and your eyelids close. Already, your breath fractures as you reach inside. His fingers reach for your shirt buttons.

What happens then is less distinct. It's you I want to see. Falling blond, the fringe lapping the closed lids as his fist accelerates and your mouth opens, that catch in your breath. His lips cover yours, the scratch of stubble on your cheek something familiar, something fond. And I envy that kiss, this tenderness. The thick vein that I have trailed with my tongue courses inside his fist. It pulses for him. His grip stronger than mine.

And when it's finished, after you share a sameness with him and your hands lace, sticky, I worry about what it is you say. Whether you touch him the way you touch me. I don't want to think they spend the night, these pick-ups something stinging in the crease of my mouth these pick-ups and strangers. Yet I don't want to think of you alone. It feels terrible to think of you alone. And I know somewhere deeper that's all you want too. What I imagine is nothing as real as that longing, as what you're really looking for. The thing is that it is not, will never be me. The feeling of coming home.

Should be more careful. Almost drop the cup.

It's cold now anyway, unpleasant to touch. Only fit for throwing away. I notice the crack on the rim when I cross to the sink, the red stain there. Little red trail against the eggshell blue. When I put my hand up to my face there's more. My mouth is bleeding. I rinse the cup, wipe my mouth, turn off the tap. Dark as hell out there: the guttering and dead leaves breaking off their branches. Steam growing from my breath against the pane. Trying not to think too much. Not to worry.

I need to talk to you.
I try not to reach for the phone.

THOMAS HEALY

from

rolling

In Glasgow. Where I saw, I would have required blinkers not to have
seen, my old flame, Nancy. I saw her first, a surprise, a week or so
after I came home, in the shoe shop where she worked. I had no idea.
The shop was not local. She wore a cotton smock. Blue. Knee-length.
It went with her eyes. We did not speak. An icy silence. Strangers.
And afterwards, on the street, passing, it was the same. There was
nothing there, not even a dislike, and not long after that I heard that
she was married.

Her brother was still pally, but he was changed – dear Christ how
changed – lanky now and with a foxy look so that what appeal he had
was gone forever. I was embarrassed in his company, so avoided him
and he got the message.

I was getting the message. I had seen too much of hardship. I
determined to improve my lot, make money. I wanted a car, good
clothes, tickets for the London fights. But that kind of money you
would never get, not working for someone else. It took me all of a day
to reason that. So I quit my job to open a second-hand shop. I bought
and sold anything and everything, and soon, in a remarkably short
time, I had four second-hand shops and all of them made money. They
made a lot of money, not always from honest dealing. I doubt whether

there are any second-hand shops that you can call honest, you work too close a fence, with stolen stuff, you want to make quick money. And the same with scrap metal – bought a half share in a scrap-metal yard and it made more money than the four shops put together.

At 19 years old I had my car, one of that year, good clothes, the money for travel, for the London fights, and if I gloss over this, success of a sort, it is because I think it fitting. I did not drink. I made money. There was nothing in my later drinking, near hobo state, I can blame on that time.

From 16 to 19 I had no cause or wish to drink. Life was good, no complications. I read still, still stayed at home, but disaster in the sweetest guise, the shape of a boy, was lurking round the corner.

This was to be the worst. I could have taken anything other than that, my love for a boy, for love it was and sprung on me who did not want it – by God I didn't – in the instant of a blink.

In a snooker hall, a working man's club – I was with a couple of pals – just passing an afternoon.

You entered the place up wooden stairs. A balcony looked onto a games room below. It was grubby and shabby, a dirty floor, guys playing cards and indoor bowls. I leaned against the balcony. Smoking. I remember smoking, the click of the balls, the waft of the smoke, how I was dressed, as when a child I remembered the carnival through the trees over the river. The clearest recall, as if time stuck in the instant that he entered. A boy who stirred me as no other boy, or girl at that time had ever stirred me, and a feeling I would never know again.

I could not from the start shift my eyes from him. I was astonished and embarrassed that I could not shift my eyes from him. He was dark with combed-down hair, a Beatle cut and still at school with a schoolbag and blazer: he wore grey flannel trousers.

I watched him play, stretch out: his head, arse and thighs, under the bright lights. I lingered there to watch him play and felt a choke in my throat, sweat on my brow. But a bastard place, the crudest talk, to admire and sneak glances at a boy, a total stranger.

My pals and I went out to a pub where, the first time for almost three years, I had a drink. It was a surprise to them and a surprise to me that I had a drink. Whisky and beer. We all three treated a round. And if shaken, downcast till then, I left that pub a new man – high-spirited, surging with power, not giving a damn.

I went back to the snooker hall with expectations, hoping to look and admire, but the boy had gone.

I think I returned to the pub. It would have been my way, after a taste of booze, wanting more, even after three years I would have wanted more. Of that I am certain. But the night is clouded, and where I went – a night in the pub, out with a girl, just a walk around – I do not know.

Next morning the boy was in my head. I smoked in bed and thought about him. All of the day, grey winter November, he was in my head. I had a few drinks at lunchtime, pints of beer and thought about him. And I wondered what the fuck was wrong with me that a boy, a stranger, a moment, could have such effect? I sat alone drinking as, in the future, I was to sit alone with many a drink and not always drinking beer. No. I had money enough for faster effect, and right from the start, from the night before, at intervals for long years after, I drank this time for sheer effect.

That night at four o'clock, I was again in the snooker hall. Standing. Leaning against the banister. And if not drunk I was not sober. Smoking. A white coat on. I knew some, most of the guys, mostly small-time thugs and thieves who loitered there and we all of us smoked, and the place, like the London joint – the gangster's parlour – was like peering through a fog.

I stood. Impatient. Big. I was if lithe much heavier now, a solid weight and if still boxing I would have fought as middle. But my mind that night was far from boxing. Waiting. I felt a freak waiting. A schoolboy with his schoolbag – what if the guys around knew my head, the purpose of my visit? It was my constant dread as time passed by, that they might twig, for it was not my scene, that place, not really, and neither was the way I felt.

I was about to go, depart, for it was long past four, when he walked in. My heart leapt. Literally. The very sight of him. I leaned back against the balcony. He wore still the blazer and his schoolbag, but had switched his pants to a light tight denim.

He seemed well known in the place, and nothing shy, rather the opposite, rather pushy – I fancied that he was pushy, a kid with spunk. Modern. His Beatle haircut, pointed shoes, tight denims – the other stuff, school blazer and bag, just made him different as a touch of class, innocence: if, as I later learned, he was far from innocent. Again, I watched him play. A closer view. He wore a blood-red jersey. His chest looked strong, but his shoulders were slender, fragile almost, and – he strained the denim with his arse and thighs – a wonderful perfection to me who felt like a monster for the observation. Study. His head, hair, the line of his brow, flare of his nose. He had the biggest impact, and I can see him still. How he was. His smile and how his hands, slender fingers, had dirty nails.

He would leave about six-thirty or seven, and I left with him – but for my evening drink.

There was a particular pub, it was just over the way, outside of the snooker hall, where – it had a quiet lounge and heartbreak music – I had chosen for my drinking.

And I drank. There was now nothing to stop me, for I had plenty of money and was legally old enough to sit in that place, indulge my habit, wonder at the boy, think the fondest thoughts. Invariably leaving I was drunk, not falling-down drunk – but drunk enough to drive too fast, to not have driven at all.

But even with no car I was drinking too much, and drinking alone, a sure depressant – I felt the depression in the mornings. But I blamed the boy and not the whisky. How could I blame the whisky when a couple more drinks and the depression lifted? Indeed, for this was a difficult time, I thought the whisky and the surcease it gave, was all that kept me going.

I went back to the snooker hall night after night. Four o'clock. Six-thirty or seven, the kid gone home, I would be in the pub. I would

stay for the music, such sad songs, for a couple of hours. Usually.
Though once I recall I stayed till shutting. I was rolling drunk that
night and the barman begged my car keys. I was by then something
of a regular, a good customer because of the money I spent. It made
a good excuse for a return next morning.

So from the start, after not a week back drinking I was also
drinking mornings. I should explain that in some Glasgow pubs, after
nights of drinking in the way I drank, you are thought a regular very
soon.

In a few pubs I was soon thought that, a regular. Inside of a week
I was up to drinking, in bar measures – I still at this time did not
drink at home – a bottle a day and some days more. That's not
counting the beer and I drank a lot of beer. Especially in the morning
I drank a lot of beer. That was for the first week. The second week I
was drinking more, an all-day thing, morning till night, but drinking
the best – a five-star malt – it did not hit me as it should. It took years
to hit me as it should.

There was even in the first week's drinking some pride in the liquor
I could hold. I thought about other guys, what booze it took to make
them fall, and that I was tougher, stronger. In any case I suffered little,
just as I said from the morning blues and I thought I knew the cause
of them.

Looking back, but for that boy I would not have drunk, not then,
and might never have drunk.

As it was, my frightful lust – for no other boy or male would
trouble me again – I didn't know what way to turn and the bottle was
my only solace.

After a week or two of nightly visits at four o'clock I was playing
the kid at snooker. His name was Tony. He was easy and free with a
nice nature, and my game was to anchor the cue ball so as to have
him stretch, lean out over the table under the lights. But it was not
enough, and, soon, I was waiting outside to run him home.

He stayed in a tenement better than mine, red sandstone facing
near Shawfield, a football stadium, and *he* asked *me* to take him out.

Daytime.

I asked about school.

'I'll dodge it.'

In my car, windows up, outside his close and I could almost feel the heat of him.

'I've dodged it before,' he told me.

'You hiv?'

'Aye.' He smiled. Conspiratorial. 'You,' he said, 'kin write me a note, say I was sick.'

I smoked.

He smoked.

I liked it that he smoked. Christ, I liked it that his nails were dirty and I would write many a sick note in days to come.

'It's best,' he said, 'daytime.'

'Is it?'

'Aye.' Again the smile, and quite a game this flirt with me. 'Besides,' he said, 'I don't like school.'

'I hated it.'

'You did?'

'Aye.'

'How old are you?' Blue-grey eyes, a quizzical look.

'Nineteen.'

'I'm fourteen.' And a sure fourteen. How he sat, looked at me, who did not run him home for nothing, gave him money, if only a little, without a motive and knew that.

My problem in those long days and drunken nights was I did not know my motive. Or I was scared to admit it, even to myself. And I did like Tony, as a person, and the more I knew him the better I liked him. Yet at the root of it all for that boy and me, and from the first, from the moment I saw him, it was a physical thing. But such a fumble, as if he were a china doll.

There was in the mind of the youth I was, a sense of ridicule in the love of a boy. How I felt just did not suit me and once again, with another lover, a deeper love, I wished that we had never met.

It was a crazy time, not him but me and my stupid act. Drinking. It got that (shades of Katie, but a lot more booze) I could not meet him sober. If I met him at noon-time I'd had a few and in my car I had a bottle. But even with the booze it was still awkward, the most awkward time (which should have been the best time) of all my life.

The thing dragged on, my drinking increased. I bought him a watch for a Christmas present. He almost hugged me for the gift and I could, I know, have held him then – at least I could have held him. But I was still so reluctant, scared that a night, a watch, might ruin it all. What? I still don't know. For sex was the root – without sex, physical attraction, there was nothing between that kid and me.

He knew, I knew: so why the fuck my fatherly act?

But it could not last. I think we both knew that it could not last. That there was nothing fatherly in my affections.

I took him sometimes, matinees, to the movies. We saw *El Cid*. January. I would turn 20 in February. If not in the nuthouse – from my nights in the pub, the sad, sad songs – I would turn 20 in February.

Tony, I saw all the time – if not in the flesh then in my head – his smile, his voice so I could concentrate on nothing. It was impossible to work. And I was drinking money and losing money and it was downhill all the way.

I, with my innocent act, a show as stupid as my drinking, mooned about like some lovesick (and I was sick all right, even Tony enquired about my drinking) moron good for violence. The bubble burst. I could take no more, sick in the soul and sick in the head, the night that Ali (then Clay) fought Sonny Liston.

I asked Tony who he thought would win.

'Liston.'

'I think Clay.'

It was late. I was drunk. It was one of the few late nights we had together. In my car, outside the snooker hall, where at ten o'clock or closer to eleven I had picked him up. It was late anyway to buy a morning newspaper. Clay and Liston were on the front page. Liston looked a bear but I thought to see something in Clay. Tony saw something in me, the booze I had shifted – an all-day session – and not the man or youth he knew. No. I was drunk all right and tougher, more rough with him and I could be very rough, much rougher than he knew. I had not my car and the trimmings for nothing. He said not a word, no protests, I drove him to a place I knew, where before, with girls, I had been.

When it was over I felt so lousy I can't explain.

'You still think Liston?'

The night was dark.

Tony said nothing.

You could hear the wind, the gusts outside.

I drank some whisky from the bottle I kept.

Outside the night, the wind and rain.

Tony sat smoking. In the half-light. Tears glistened on his cheeks. I loved him more than ever. Then. In my car. And there was nothing dirty or perverted about it, just how in my roughness I'd bruised his pride and hurting him had hurt myself.

I was still half drunk and getting drunker. It was one of the times I was scared to get sober. I was just 19, too young for this and the pain I felt for that boy that night, feeling so roguish, dirty, near suicidal.

'You feel okay?'

'It's late,' he said.

'I'll get you home.'

Driving. I should not have been driving. Swigging at whisky. And how I felt, like that, that boy and me, a head-on smash might solve it all.

Playing music. Smoking. I drove with no lights. Tony pointed it out. I switched them on. He told me that I drove too fast.

'You want to get home.'

'I want tae get home alive.'

I slowed a bit.

'It's okay,' Tony said. 'I mean, you know –'

'Sure.'

'You're –'
'What?'
'I don't know.'
'I know what you mean.'
'You do?'
'I think so.'
'Nobody'll know.'
'No.' I wanted to hold and to comfort him, but it was no good with the way I felt. I knew what he meant, how I'd caught him, ragged underwear, and his stupid shame just added more weight to the load that I carried. 'Not if you don't tell them they won't!'

I dropped him off outside his close.

Late.

It must have been two, three o'clock, easily two or three o'clock, for I remember I asked him what he would say – where he had been.

I got drunk next day, or still drinking that morning, I did not sober up. Clay beat Liston and I had a bet, £100 at 7–1 that Clay would beat Liston. It was two weeks or more before I collected. I got so drunk. But again, and again must stress, not falling-down drunk. I just lost interest. It was my first true bender. In a hotel. I just booked in and spoke to no one.

But my head nagged me. The sober moments were early mornings. For I knew it was all wrong. Holed-up drinking, guzzling whisky and I had jilted Tony, a date we had. It was a mean time. The hotel was good, it cost me plenty, but a miserable time, never going out, just drinking in the bar and in my room. The recall is fogged, but the fear that I was queer was very real indeed.

At the end of a week, eight days, no fun in the drunk – few of my drunks were ever fun – I sobered up enough to go home. I had no sweats, shakes, no sickness, nothing – just a dead feeling at the end of the bout. For a day or two I could not eat. Small penance for my orgy of drink: no reason to quit, though for a time I did slow down, cut back on the morning drinking.

The Gorbals now was a heap of rubble, that and brand-new houses, tower blocks, and where I stayed – my mother, her tenement, was last to move – was truly grim.

Yet it seemed impossible to get her out.

Eight months, a year, we had lived alone in the tenement. A spooky place. All the other houses doors open, like living in a ghost town. The water cut off and we had to carry our own, and still – without toilets – my mother would not move.

I was worried, with reason, for one light in a tenement and winos squatting, moving in, guys needy or greedy, crazy, might kill you for a sixpence.

So nights I stayed with my mother. Who would not go. Move out. The most stubborn stand. She held up the work, tumble of a hundred years, the demolition of the tenement. I thought it funny and sad, councillors visiting, the housing threatening. I forget how much (a figure was quoted) she cost them a day. But it went on. I got used to it, the last stand in the tenement. Though, nights in a high wind, the whole place swayed and I got drunk sometimes and listened to music, the Beatles and Stones, something new in that old house two windows high.

It was no councillor's plea – the threatening housing, and they did threaten, finally got my mother out.

My sister, she had a boyfriend of the snooty sort who was ashamed, mortified at the place she stayed in. So we moved, or she moved, a shift, not far – two miles at most – to a house with a loo, a bath, hot water and safety. No winds there or winds that threatened. I went to a flat, a place of my own. It was the end of an era, where the place that long was home was now empty sky.

I was by this time, March, drinking steadily, heavily, and there is no doubt that booze was the motivating factor in what happened next. I sold out on the shops, my share of the scrap metal, I sold the lot to my partner, a hard-faced crook, for a crazy price to do a more crazy thing. I ran away. I was such a fool and a coward. The finest feeling I ever knew. And what the fuck did it really matter that it was a boy and not a girl?

I pause. Query my motives, how then I felt or thought to feel, for not only booze but age creeps in.

Certainly if there had been no booze I would not have sold out, not all that I had and not at the price. At a time when I did not need the money.

But I was all caught up with a need to escape for I was not happy. There was some sense of unease. All the other guys, they went with girls. I was stuck on Tony and if I did not flaunt him, I did not hide him either.

But the whole thing and I was only 20 – and, I liked to think, a man's man – still puzzles me.

I will say no more of Tony. If I ran from him or ran from myself, but drop him now as I dropped him then. Sudden. He came and went if, a long time, even now, he lingers on, a good and healthy memory.

a boy's own story

JACK DICKSON

JACK DICKSON

Nick couldn't remember a time when *he* hadn't been there. In his life. In the house. With him. On him. In him.

This is how fathers show love for their sons, *he'd* said.

Nick had no reason to doubt him. It was all he knew. All he'd ever known.

He had food in his belly. A roof over his head. Clothes on his back.

The cock in his arse must have hurt, the first time. But Nick couldn't remember.

Couldn't remember a time when *he* hadn't been there. When things hadn't been this way. Sometimes, even then, he was left alone. In their big bed at night. But the man he called dad always came home. The next day. Or the day after.

Nick loved his father, because that's what sons do. And his father loved him back.

He had uncles.

This is how uncles show love for their nephews, they'd said.

The uncles came and went . . . went and came inside him. Through it all, his father was there. With him. Holding him in bed at night, a thick hairy arm around Nick's five-year-old chest.

He liked school. He did well at school. His father enrolled him, at six. And Nick went, because boys went to school.

Boys also washed their own clothes, cooked and cleaned and sometimes fell asleep at their desks. Nick was quiet, well-behaved, no trouble at all. The teachers barely noticed him. And his classmates finally took the hint when he shrugged away their offers of friendship for the hundredth time.

Boys don't need friends.

Boys only need their father.

He couldn't remember exactly when things had started to go wrong. When his father started not to like him. Maybe 10. Maybe 11. His uncles were around more. One uncle in particular, who intervened when Nick tried to crawl into his father's arms and his father punched him in the side of the head.

He started doing things. Stupid things. Like answering back. Like asking why he never had a birthday, the way the kids at school did. Like why they never had a tree. And what was Christmas.

His father would scream at him, hit him again. Nick threw himself around his father's legs, held on until a kick sent him sprawling across the room.

One Uncle In Particular held him afterwards, stroking his young cock and kissing him. It wasn't the same. But it was something. And Nick knew his father would come back. Maybe more drunk. Maybe angrier than ever. But he would come back.

And he did. And for a while it would be good again. Nick stopped doing the stupid things. But it didn't help because there was one thing he couldn't stop.

He was growing up. And there was nothing either of them could do about that.

One Uncle In Particular was around more and more. Nick slept with him more and more, when the first tufts of hair appeared in his deep armpits. His father was around less and less. But Nick knew he'd come back.

About that time, he started secondary school. One Uncle In

Particular came along to Parents' Night. He sat with Nick during the welcoming speeches, smiled and chatted and sipped wine with the other parents afterwards, a paternal hand on Nick's shoulder.

But he wasn't his father. Nick knew that. He was, however, the next best thing.

Nick was good at art. Good at music. He did his homework, was always clean and tidy.

With the onset of puberty, he escaped the rash of acne which plagued his classmates. Nick grew from a beautiful boy into a handsome, if skinny, teenager. One Uncle In Particular liked the new Nick. He liked the way the new Nick's body arched under his when they fucked.

His father never came around much, these days. And when he did, it was to talk to One Uncle In Particular. If Nick made any overture, he got a fist in his belly and a session in the cupboard under the stairs.

They never marked his face. Even then, they knew not to.

Like they'd known to enrol him in school. And even if anything was ever noticed – which it wasn't – all the visitor from Social Services would see was a single parent trying to bring up a kid the best he could.

About 13 or 14, Nick discovered girls. And he began to talk to his classmates – not talk, so much, as listen.

And Nick found out not all boys slept with their fathers.

About the same time, One Uncle In Particular started hitting him. Not much, at first. Mainly when Nick wanted sex. When Nick's hand moved towards One Uncle In Particular's fat stubby cock before it was guided there. So Nick took the beatings. To get the sex. To get One Uncle In Particular's arms around him afterwards.

The One Uncle In Particular left too.

Nick couldn't remember when, exactly. He was used to spending time on his own, either locked in the cupboard under the stairs or squirreled away with whatever scraps of paper and stubs of pencils he could find.

He cooked. He washed. He cleaned the house. He went to school.

And when the landlord turned up, wanting the month's rent, Nick said give me a couple of days.

He was tall for his age. He was hungry. He knew what to do. He knew what was expected of him. So after the man in the park had sucked his cock, Nick took the guilt money and stocked up on essentials.

Five quid didn't go far.

Ten went further.

By the time the landlord returned, Nick had just about enough for next month's rent.

But he slept alone, at nights. And he dreamed of his father.

Nick discovered bars. The tricks came easily after that, drawn to the hollow-cheeked boy with the long legs who said he was 16. Or 18. Or 12. Or whatever age they needed him to be. Some of them he fucked because he liked them. Most he fucked to get money. The majority hurried away afterwards, leaving their spunk in knotted condoms on the ground behind Nick's bare arse. Some bought him a burger before sloping back to their wives or their boyfriends. A few looked into his eyes and wondered. None went further than that.

He was quieter at school. His clothes were old, but always clean. His homework was always done, but he never smiled.

Nick couldn't remember when he'd started drinking. Probably in the bars. It helped, at nights. Helped get him to sleep. Helped blur the nightmares. He drank beer because his father had drank beer. And he made the rent every month. Paid the gas bill. The electricity bill. The council tax was up to date.

At school, the girls liked Nick. So he fucked them too. It was strange to press his face against breasts after years of hard, hairy chests. But they were warm. And they held him afterwards.

Then someone noticed Nick. Someone noticed the quiet, clever boy with the wan face and the clean but old clothes.

Mr Matheson began talking to Nick, after English class.

Nick liked the attention. Nick put his hand on Mr Matheson's cock.

Scott Matheson moved the hand and started asking questions.

Nick made sure he was first out of English class after that.

Scott Matheson caught him in the corridor, between classes. He gave Nick his phone number. Nick crumpled the piece of paper up, then smoothed it out and put it behind the mantelpiece clock at home. And got on with his life.

So many cocks in his mouth. In his arse. His own cock fucking countless faces, holes without number. He could read them like a book, the tricks. It was just a matter of time before he met closed covers.

It was a Friday. The trick beat him 'til he could barely stand, fucked him through the pain and when he couldn't get hard anymore, balled one ragged-nail fist and fucked him with that.

Nick staggered home in a daze. He curled into a ball on the bed, feeling the trick's echo inside him all through the hours of darkness. No arms around him. But no nightmares either. Next morning, he wadded up toilet paper and slid it into his underpants. By noon he'd had to change it four times. His head hurt. And something like panic churned in his stomach.

The clock on the mantelpiece swam before his eyes. It took a while, but he made it to the phone box on the corner.

Scott Matheson found him there, ten minutes after Nick had managed to punch in the numbers.

'Casualty' doctors are overworked and underpaid. They looked at Scott a bit funny, but let him stay with Nick as a frowning nurse stitched the tears in the lining of Nick's rectum and bathed his bruises. All Nick knew was a hand around his and the smell of the same disinfectant he used to clean the kitchen.

Scott took him home.

To Scott's house.

Nick ran away as soon as his legs would let him.

Scott came round. To Nick's house. With Social Services. Nick looked at all the people on his couch and wondered where they had come from.

He was 16, according to the school records. Not their responsibility.

Scott took Nick home a second time. To Scott's house.

Nick stayed.

After the third attempt to creep into Scott's bed, he gave up. And the nightmares came back. But he stayed anyway.

Scott's wife was dead. Ovarian cancer. Scott's sons were all grown up. Scott was due to retire, after the summer holidays.

Scott was the only man not to want to fuck Nick. It made Nick uneasy.

Scott was lonely. He needed a project.

Scott petitioned to legally adopt Nick.

Nick went back to school, after two weeks' recuperation.

Scott paid private investigators to dig into Nick's past, as part of the adoption process. They never found any trace of the man Nick called father, who had enrolled Nick at school. The house where he'd lived for as long as he could remember was rented in the same name. There was no birth certificate, but they found a date on the school enrolment form.

On 28 August that year, Nick celebrated his first birthday. Scott gave him a camera. Nick looked through the eyepiece and saw a way of framing his world.

By 28 August the following year, Nick was attending a local college, studying history of art and photography. And Scott arranged and paid for therapy.

Nick and the therapist eyed each other.

The therapist let Nick draw when the words wouldn't come.

But the nightmares did. They'd never really stopped.

Scott's sons fought their father's attempts to adopt the sullen-faced rent-boy. Scott won. His sons slowly accepted their new stepbrother. Scott was pleased. Nick barely noticed.

Scott felt he could give a second chance at life to the talented, damaged teenager.

Nick no longer felt at all. And in the second term of his first year of college, he met Carl in the back room of a bar.

Carl was older. But younger than Scott. And younger than Nick's father.

Carl felt the need in Nick straight away.

Nick saw a handsome man in a black leather jacket who looked at him the way his father and his uncles had. Nick was still tricking, still dating college girls. For the sex. For the holding afterwards.

Carl had been into bdsm for 20 years. With his collection of tawses and quirts, dildos and iron shackles handmade by a gay couple in San Francisco. With his Foucault and his literature. His sub-dom theorising. Controlling men who wanted to be boys made Carl's cock twitch. Breaking them to his will made it twitch more. The beautiful 19-year-old with the hard knowing eyes and the defiant stance threw down a gauntlet to the older, more experienced player.

It was a game.

A game played by men.

With rules. Boundaries. A soft, secure arena.

After their first scene, Carl threw the safety net away. He didn't stand a chance. Neither of them did. He was out of his depth with Nick. From the moment he'd chained him to the wall of his basement, delivered the whipping of his life then held Nick sobbing and hard in his arms, Carl's feet never touched bottom again. And when he collared Nick a week later and took him on as his boy, Carl had no idea what Nick was doing.

Neither had Nick. Not then.

Scott did. Scott worried. He didn't know about Carl. But he knew there was something. The therapist told him to expect a period of adjustment. The therapist advised no interference. And Nick was still attending college. Carl insisted on that. So Scott gave what he always gave.

Unconditional love.

As he opened the door to the cage.

One door opens, another closes.

So many doors, so many compartments in Nick's head. In Nick's life.

So many links. Punishment-reward. Punishment-punishment-reward.

Carl admired this. Admired the way Nick played. The way he could switch off when Carl walked out at the end of a scene. He never knew he was every man who'd ever fucked or hurt or held Nick since he was old enough to have thought.

Every man who'd ever left. Every man Nick had driven away.

Nick didn't have the vocabulary to tell him. Nick couldn't even tell himself the biggest cock in the world couldn't fill the hole inside him.

For Carl, it was every pop-psychology power dynamic theory come true.

No need to talk.

No need to negotiate.

Both were already well inside the other's head. Instinctively. Carl knew what Nick wanted, even when Nick didn't.

But he didn't know why. Or how much.

So he pushed the boundaries a little.

They could both do with the stretching.

The first time Carl chained Nick to the bed and made him watch as he fucked another man, Nick closed his eyes.

Carl slapped them open, broke his own rule and marked Nick's face.

But at least Nick got the attention.

The second time, Nick watched the sex.

He even watched Carl stroke and hold the 42-year-old boy in his arms afterwards.

Then he left, gouged two vertical slits in his right forearm with a broken bottle.

Carl found him, staged and bleeding on the doorstep.

Carl took him to 'Casualty', the way Scott had.

Carl was more scared than Scott had ever been.

Scott never knew. Nick wore long sleeves for four months after that.

Carl should have stopped then. But Carl was in as deep as Nick.

For four years they danced with but around each other.

For four years, Nick and his therapist were wallflowers, either side of a room.

Carl began to see something beneath Nick's icy, hard exterior.

He thought it was defiance. He thought defiance was there to be broken.

Nick graduated from college. His stepdad and his stepbrothers took him out for a meal. His end-of-year portfolio caught the eye of a scout from a city advertising agency. Nick got a commission.

Nick had talent.

Nick photographed through a skewed lens. But the art director could use this.

The cuts on his arm had almost healed when Carl's eye was caught by another boy.

A prettier boy.

A less fucked-up boy.

A boy who liked Mahler and hill-walking.

Nick knew Carl had others. The way he knew his father had others.

Had gone to one of those others, when he'd left Nick.

When Carl chained Nick to the bed and made him watch this time, Nick tried to hurt himself there and then.

Carl shackled his wrists to prevent it.

The prettier boy's cock hardened further. He admired the way these two played. The intensity of their game awed him.

When Nick screamed, Carl slapped then gagged him.

Then ignored him.

This time Nick used a kitchen knife and pills, in the privacy of his room at home, when he knew Scott was visiting his son.

Only luck brought Scott home early.

Nick woke up in hospital, still screaming, four days later.

When Scott finally convinced the Psychiatric Registrar Nick was fit to come home, Nick spent weeks trying to find Carl.

But Carl had left.

The way his father had left. His uncles. One Uncle In Particular.
Scott held Nick and stroked his hair.

Slowly, Nick let him.

The woman from the advertising agency accepted a bronchitis
excuse and rescheduled the shoot.

Scott found a new therapist. Who made Nick draw more. And had
other new approaches.

Nick spent Christmas with his stepdad and his stepbrothers, and
their wives. He spent Easter with his stepdad, his stepbrother, his step-
sister-in-law and his step-nephew. He still couldn't get used to holidays.
He still couldn't get used to standing in front of a mirror every morning,
intoning I love myself. I am a good person. I am worth loving.

But he did both.

For Scott.

Scott, who had stayed longer than any other man ever had. Scott
who would not sleep with him, where every other man had. Scott
who had taken him in, put him through college, paid for endless
years of therapy.

Scott who was always there. And always would be there.

The woman at the advertising agency showed Nick's work to a
friend, another art director. He phoned Nick, introduced himself as
Matt. Nick got a second commission. The scars on his arms faded but
he still wore long sleeves.

Nick sometimes dated. Women. And men. Mostly men. He hovered
on the fringes of the city's bdsm scene, half-looking for Carl, still
tricking although no money changed hands. Now he left them before
they left him. They seemed to like it that way. He never saw Carl again.

And the hole inside skinned over a bit. Still there. Just a bit less
achy. But the nightmares still came. And Nick still drank. But in
moderation.

Matt was puzzled by the gangly 24-year-old with the body of a
man and the eyes of a wee boy. He was aroused by Nick, physically
and artistically.

When Nick slept with Matt for the first time, Matt fucked him hard then held him afterwards. Because that was the way Matt fucked. When Nick refused to stay the night, Matt didn't fight it.

He phoned. They talked, about art. They worked together again. They slept together again.

Nick left in the middle of the night.

Matt let him. And called the next day.

Nick told his stepdad he'd met someone. A man. Scott told Nick's therapist. The therapist thought it would be good for Nick to attend group therapy.

For survivors of abuse.

Nick fought it, but went to please Scott. He sat in a room with a semi-circle of people who told him he wasn't gay, that he was merely reliving the abuse and to find himself a good woman.

Nick knew how he felt with a man's arms around him. He walked out of the room and never went back.

A week later, Scott met Matt.

A month after that, Nick moved into the loft Matt rented, with Scott's blessing. Nick stopped cruising. Stopped tricking in the city's bdsm bars. It was hard. And not hard. Matt's friends looked askance at Matt when he introduced Nick. They thought he was a junkie.

He was.

And detox is always painful. Nick still dreamt of his father. But now he could no longer remember his face.

One night, a year later, Scott was driving home from an evening at Nick and Matt's loft.

Scott was teetotal. The driver of the other car was five times over the legal limit. They both died instantaneously.

So did part of Nick. He'd done it again. He'd driven another man away. He refused to go to the funeral. It took him two years to even visit the grave. And he waited for his new stepbrothers to leave too.

But they didn't. Scott had made both his sons swear, years ago, that when he went, Nick would remain part of the family.

They never broke their promise.

They accepted Matt, too.

And Nick started to paint. He wants to destroy the canvases afterwards. Matt rescues them, sells them to private collectors who are, like him, drawn to the dark swirling images.

Matt and Nick are still together. Six years now. Nick drinks less. Matt bought him seeds. Nick has a garden in containers on the edge of the loft roof. This year he grew lavender and moon flowers. Both thrive.

Matt bought Nick a canary.

The canary thrives. Not everything Nick touches dies or goes away.

Nick still has nightmares. He may never sleep normally. But he paints at night, when the dreams are very bad.

Nick still likes to be restrained during sex. He still aches for the pain of the slap. The hole inside never really heals.

But he lets Matt love him. Because he is worth loving. And Matt refuses to let Nick drive him away.

free love

ALI SMITH

The first time I ever made love with anyone it was with a prostitute in Amsterdam. I was 18 and her name was Suzi, I don't think she was much older than I was. I had been cycling round the town in a bad mood and had come upon the red light district quite by chance; it was the most pleasant red light district I've ever got lost in. The women there sit on chairs in windows that are lined with furs and fabrics, they sit breasts naked or near naked, draped with gowns and furs. It took me a while to work out that they were probably scowling at me so contemptuously not just because I was staring but because I wasn't business.

It was evening and I'd been out cycling by myself. I had wandered down a back street and had stopped to put my jumper on, and my bike had fallen over and the chain had come off. It was when I stood the bike up against the wall of a building to get a proper go at the chain that I noticed the cards stuck by the door. Several of them were in English, one said: 'Need To Relax? Take It Easy. No Rush. Ring Becky.' Another said: 'Dieter Gives Unbeatable Service. Floor 2.' Another said something about uniforms and domination and had a drawing of a schoolgirl on it. I was just laughing at them to myself when I saw one at the bottom in tiny handwriting and several languages, Dutch, French, German, English and something eastern, and the English line said 'Love for men also women, Suzi 3rd floor'. The 'also' was underlined.

That's when I left my bike standing and found myself going up the old staircase; on the third floor there was a door with the same card stuck on it and my hand was knocking on the door. I had a story ready in my head in case I wanted to get away, I was going to say I was lost and could she direct me back to the youth hostel. But she came to the door and she was so nice, I took to her at once and wasn't the least bit scared.

The flat had one room and a bathroom off it, some chairs and the bed had a hanging bead thing curtaining off the kitchen area like in photographs of the '60s. On the wall there was a poster of the lead singer from A-Ha. A-Ha were big at the time in Europe and she said she liked him because he was a man but he looked like a woman. I remember I thought that was a very exciting thing to say. I hadn't heard anyone say anything direct like that before. I come from a small town; one night my friend Jackie and I had been sitting in a pub and two girls had been sitting at a table on the other side of the room; they looked conventional, more so than we did really, they had long hair, were wearing a lot of make-up, and it was when I glanced to see what kind of footwear they had on that I noticed one of them had one foot out of her high-heeled shoe and was running it up and down the other one's shin under the table. This was a very brave thing to be doing now that I come to think about it; chances are if anyone had seen them they'd have been beaten up. At the time I pointed it out to Jackie and she said something about how disgusting it was, I think I even agreed, I never wanted to disagree with her on anything.

The prostitute spoke English with an American accent. She said she had an hour and would that be enough for me, and though I hadn't a clue I said yes I thought so. I showed her my hands all oily from the bike and said I should maybe wash them, and she sat me down in one of the old armchairs and, bringing a cloth and a washing-up bowl over, washed and dried them for me. Then she did this thing, she put my hand to her mouth and put her tongue between my fingers at the place where my fingers meet my hand, and she pushed it in, going along between each. I think my head almost blew off just at her doing that.

She gave me a cup of very strong coffee and a glass of red wine, she told me to help myself from the bottle of wine she left on the little table next to the chair, then she put her arms around my neck and kissed me, and loosened my clothes, and undid my jeans, and I sat there amazed. She took my hand and took me on to the bed, she didn't even pull the covers back, we stayed on top, it was August, warm, and afterwards she showed me what to do back though I did have a pretty good idea. When eventually she looked at her watch and at me and smiled and shrugged her shoulders, we got dressed again and I took out my wallet and thumbed through the guilder, but she put her hand over mine and closed the wallet up. It's free, she said, the first time should always be free, and when she saw me to the door she said would I be in Amsterdam long and would I like to come back. I said I would very much like to, and went down the stairs in such a daze that when I came to my bike I got on it and tried to cycle it away, completely forgot about the chain and nearly hit my chin off the handlebars. So I pushed it back to the youth hostel and I felt as I walked past the reflections of the tall buildings curving in the leafy surfaces of the canals that life was wondrous, filled with possibility. I stopped there and leaned on the railings and watched the late sun hitting the water, shimmering apart and coming together again in the same movement, at the same moment.

When I arrived back at the hostel Jackie put the chain back on for me. Jackie and I had been friends since school, she'd been in the year above me, and we'd stayed friends now we were both students. We'd saved our summer money to go on this trip. I'd been serving in the souvenir shop on the caravan site since the end of June and she'd been behind the bed and breakfast counter of the tourist information board; we made a pittance but it was enough to get us return tickets for a cheap overnight bus to Amsterdam.

Jackie was blonde and boyish and golden in those days. One day I had simply seen her, she was sitting on the school wall by the main door and I had thought she looked like she was surrounded with yellow light, like she had been gently burnt all over with a fine fire. At a party we'd sat in a dark corner and Jackie had nudged my arm, her eyes directing me to a handsome thuggy boy lounging on the couch opposite watching us, her mouth at my ear whispering the words, see him? Tonight I only have to smile, you know, that's all I have to do.

I had thought this very impressive, and had held her head for her later in the upstairs bathroom when she was being sick after drinking a mixture of beer and wine; we sat on the stairs laughing after that at the girl whose party it was going round the living-room hoovering up other people's sick into one of those small car hoovers; after that we had been friends. I don't know why she liked me, I think because I was quiet and dark and everybody thought I must be clever. I'd thought Jackie was beautiful, I thought she looked like Jodie Foster on whom I had had a crush, she looked like Jodie Foster only better. I'd thought that when we were at school and I thought it then, even though Jodie Foster's film career had hit rather a low spot at the time.

I'd had these thoughts for years and they were getting harder and harder to keep silent about. I didn't really have a choice. Once we got to Amsterdam and she saw there were people selling big lumps of hash in the street she was filled with moral outrage, that's what she was like. But the overnight bus had been a great excuse to lean my head on her shoulder, to have my nose in her yellow hair and pretend I was asleep, which meant I was very tired the first day we were in Amsterdam, going round in a stupor telling myself it was worth it.

Already Jackie had made contact with a boy from Edinburgh whom we met in the youth hostel kitchen, his name was Alan; already they were big friends and he'd suggested she should go and watch him sword-fight at a tournament that night, which is why I cycled off in a terrible mood. I was in really rather a good mood by the time I came back to the hostel, and Jackie, who hadn't gone to the sword fight after all, went into a sulk because I was happy for some reason and because when she asked me where I'd been I wouldn't tell her.

Nothing could spoil my holiday after that, I didn't care any more. And that's when Jackie started being unusually nice to me; this was confusing because although we were best friends we were pretty horrible to each other most of the time. The next day she hired a bike too and we cycled up and down by the canals and the crammed parked cars, we drank beer and ate ice-cream under restaurant parasols, we visited the Van Gogh Museum and Rembrandt's House and the Rijksmuseum full of old Dutch paintings, we went to a shop where they made shoes while you watched. The day after, we cycled to a modern art gallery; downstairs they had a room sculpture where people were sitting around a bar and their faces were made of clocks. We wandered this gallery for a while and upstairs I lost Jackie and fell asleep on one of the wooden seats. When I woke up she was sitting very close to me, her arms on my shoulder. I sat up and she didn't move away; we sat there looking at the picture I'd fallen asleep in front of, it was a huge rectangle of red paint with one thin strip of blue paint down the left-hand side. Her leg was pressing firmly into my leg. Do you like this she asked, looking at the picture, and said I did, and she suggested we should go and visit the Heineken factory now.

At the Heineken factory they give you a tour of where and how the beer is made, all the steps in its brewing process, how it's bottled, how the labels are stuck on and where it goes after that. At each stage they give you a generous glass of beer and everyone on the tour shouts cheers or *pröst* and drinks it. Then they take you into their office for after-tour drinks. By the time we'd done the Heineken tour we were so drunk we shouldn't have been cycling at all and had to leave the bikes against a tree and lie on our backs in a park, laughing at nothing and looking at the sky. It wasn't as if we'd never been drunk together before, but somehow this time it was different, and we sat on the grass in the late afternoon and I told her all the things I'd felt for years now, and she looked at me woundedly, as if I'd slapped her, and told me she felt exactly the same. Then she put her arms round me and kissed my mouth and my neck and shoulders, we were kissing in the middle of Amsterdam and nobody even noticing. Even after the Heineken wore off the afternoon didn't, it lasted for the rest of the holiday, me with my arm through hers on the street, at nights in the youth hostel dormitory Jackie reaching up from her bunk below mine to press her hand into my back, us holding hands between bunks in the dark in a room full of sleeping people. Very romantic. Amsterdam was very romantic. We took photos of each other at the fish market, I still have that photo somewhere. We went boating on a lake and took pictures of each other rowing.

The day before we were supposed to be leaving, on the pretext of going out to do some mysterious present buying I cycled back to the red light district and left my bike at the bottom of the stairs again. I had to wait this time for half an hour. Suzi remembered me, I know for sure because afterwards she sat up, looked at her watch, smiled and ruffled my hair, saying, it's sad darling but the second time you have to pay. It was good, but not as good as the first, and it cost me a fortune. On top of which I had to buy Jackie a present; I remember it was expensive but I can't remember what it was I actually bought her. I think it was a ring.

Of course when we got home we stopped being able to do things like hold each other's arm in the street, though we did manage to snatch a little time after hours in the back gardens of unsuspecting people, in lanes and alleyways between houses or garages, in the back of her father's van parked in the dark by the river. Otherwise it was downstairs at either of our houses after everybody else had gone to bed, on the floor or the couch, one of us with hand over the other's mouth, both of us holding and catching our breath.

The first place we really made love was arriving back home after Amsterdam in the women's toilets at the bus station, hands inside clothes, pushed up against the wall and the locked door in the minutes before her father was due to come and take us and our rucksacks home. It was one of the most exciting things I have ever done in my life, though Jackie always called it our sordid first experience. About a month after, I walked past the tourist information board and saw through the window in the back office Jackie heavily kissing the boy who worked in the Caledonian Canal tourist boats. I thought that remarkably sordid, I remember. But then, what people think is sordid is relative after all; the person who saw us holding hands between our seats at the theatre one night thought it sordid enough to tell our mothers about us in anonymous letters. We both had a lot of denying to do and that's something that certainly brought us closer together at the time. We had that to thank them for. Recently Jackie and I lived in the same city again for a while, and we were always nice to each other when we'd meet occasionally in the street. We both know we owe each other that, at least.

But I date the beginning of my first love from that August in Amsterdam, and we lasted for over five years on and off before we let go. I think about it from time to time, and when I do the picture that comes first to mind is one of the sun as it breaks apart and coheres on the waters of an unknown city, and I'm myself, a smile all over my face, my wallet in my pocket still full of clean new notes.

IRVINE WELSH
IRVINE WELSH

marabou
stork
nightmares

I scored an ecky and went out with a couple of fringe cashies who were into clubbing, to this new midweek club at The Venue. I was relieved to be away. It was okay, but I recognised yet another cunt, and this time got an even bigger shock. This boy was well into his dancing. I went up and spoke to him. I don't know who was the most surprised, myself or Bernard. He was really E'd n aw. I found myself, to my surprise, hugging him. Bernard and I had never touched like this before, just exchanged blows in makeshift boxing rings. We farted around on the dance floor, enjoying the hip-hop beat. I'm mair ay a hardcore than a garagey or hip-hop type ay cunt myself, but this was okay. We talked for a long time and my cashie mates filtered away, so Bernard and I ended up leaving and headed down to Chapps, a gay club near the Playhouse.

—Nivir thoat ah'd see you eckied up, Roy, he said.

—Oan it non-stoap fir the last six months, I told him with a sad smile. Bernard was all right.

—Nivir thoat ah'd be in here, though. I smiled, looking around. I didn't like the place. I told Bernard that I thought it was pretty sad and desperate, the way all those queens cruised each other out.

–Naw, it isnae really, he explained – cause here just about every guy who wants fucked ends up getting fucked. It's much sadder and more desperate up at Buster Brown's or any hetro place, cause the number of guys that want fucked is higher than the number of lassies that want to fuck them. At least here, most people get what they want.

I thought about that for a while. There was no doubting his logic. I had to agree. It was easy. I felt good. I was rushing on the E. – Whoahh, man, that ecky . . .

–Well, it agrees wi ye, he laughed.

I looked at him and said, slipping my arm around his neck – Listen, Bernard, you're all right, man, ken? You had the whole thing sussed way back. I was a fuckin wanker. I couldna handle anything. I'm no just talking aboot you bein a buft . . . eh, bein gay, I jist mean everything . . . aw fuck, Bernard, I'm really sorry, man . . . it's not the E talking, ah've just fucked things up, Bernard . . .

He shrugged. – We aw fuck things up, Roy.

–Naw, bit see, when yuv *really* fucked things up, fucked them up so bad so as that thir's nothing ye kin ever dae tae pit it right; just nothing, man, like it's always with ye? Bernard, see when ye dae something bad, dae something terrible, it doesnae make ye a bad person, does it? Ah mean ye can change, right?

–Ah suppose ye can, Roy . . . what's wrong, Roy? What is it? Yir talking aboot love, eh?

I thought bitterly about that, – Nah, no love, the reverse ay that, I smiled, then I gave him a tight hug. He reciprocated.

–Ah nivir goat tae know ye, Bernard. Ah acted like a cunt tae you . . .

–It worked both ways, he smiled, hugging me again. It felt good.

–But ah've changed, Bernard. I've allowed myself tae feel. That means that ah have tae dae something, like tae sort ay prove tae myself that I've changed. It's like tae assume responsibility for ending my pain and making someone else feel better. Even if it involves the greatest sacrifice. Try tae understand . . . ah mean, fuck,

from **marabou stork nightmares** 47

ah sound like the auld man gein it big licks wi one ay Churchill's fuckin speeches . . . it sounds like ah'm waffling here . . .

I just couldn't say.

—It's okay, Roy, he just kept saying, then he seemed tae go sad. — Listen, Roy, I've got the virus. I tested positive. I'm HIV.

I felt as if the life had been crushed out of my frame. — Bernard . . . naw . . . fuck . . . how . . .

—A couple ay months ago. It's cool, though . . . ah mean, it's no cool, but that's the wey it goes, eh, he shrugged, then looked at me intensely. — But it's the quality thing in life, Roy. Life's good. Hang onto life. Hang onto it, Roy, he smiled as I started to sob. — C'mon, Roy, stoap acting like a big poof! He laughed, comforting me, — it's awright, man, it's okay . . .

But it wisnae okay.

But me and Bernard, well, we were okay.

The following Friday I arranged to go to the Rezurrection gig at Ingliston with him and his posse. It was weird, Bernard and I becoming mates. His poetry was still shite, well, that's maybe no fair, but it was certainly patchy. At least he had grown out of inflicting it on people. I actually volunteered to read them. Some of it was to do with ecky and shagging; those were the best ones. The shagging poems would have disgusted me before; the idea of men doing that with each other, men shagging. Now though, it just seemed like two people in love, like me and Dorie. The queenish rants were still a bit hard to take.

Bernard's posse were an okay crowd; mixed gays and straights with a few fag-hags thrown in. The fag-hags were quite pathetic figures. There was something incomplete about them. I spotted it straightaway, it was an obscure quality, but I saw it in myself. We had some problems getting sorted with eckies, and Bernard and his posse were just into doing some speed and acid – Supermarios.

I wasn't up for the acid, – No way, man, I said to Bernard. I was remembering my bad trip.

I was remembering someone else's bad trip.

He gave me an as-you-like-it shrug.

–It's no that, Bernard, it's just that there's too much shite floatin aroon in ma heid tae dae acid the now, ken?

–Fair enough, he said. – I think you're being wise.

But I wisnae wise. I was talking to a guy in the posse called Art, a big fuckin pill-box this cunt, and I got carried away as he talked of his drug experiences. I fired down a Supermario.

At first it was great; the lights, the sounds. We headed for the heart of the bass and I was happy tripping oot ay ma box. Bernard looked fucking amazing; I tried not to think of him having that fuckin virus in him, he just looked so good. Party chicks checked him out, well fucked off he was gay. This shag in the posse called Laura shouted in my ear: – I'm madly in love with your brother. It's a shame he's gay. I still want to have his baby. I just smiled. I was enjoying her patter, even hoping that I might be a proxy fuck for Bernard.

Then I looked at the big sign above the stage.

reZurrection

The Z luminated and the slogans came rushing into my head:

**NO MAN HAS THE RIGHT
WHEN SHE SAYS NO SHE MEANS NO
THERE IS NO EXCUSE
THERE IS NEVER AN EXCUSE**

I felt terrible all of a sudden; just all hot, breathless and shaky. I tried to compose myself, moving through the crowd towards the exit and the chill-out zone. I needed to think. I needed to

A girl smiled at me, and it looked like

It was her

They all looked like her

Then there was a guy. A steward. It was Uncle Gordon. – Ah'm no fucking gaun wi you again, right! Ah'm no gaunny fuckin dae that again! I shouted at him.

–Calm doon, mate, eh, a raver shouted at me as the security guy stood bemused.

I ran to the toilets and sat in a trap crying and talking to myself. Some guys came in and talked me down. They found Bernard. I heard somebody mutter, – Cunt cannae handle his drugs.

Hospital Bed   LYING IN YOUR HOSPITAL BED IN A COMA STUPID
RELATIVES NIPPING YOUR HEAD CAN THEY
UNDERSTAND WHERE YOU HIDE AND WHAT YOUR LIFE
AMOUNTS TO

Their Africa   YOU ARE A
DYING MAN
AND YOU ASK

The Well   FOR NO PITY
ONLY UNDER-
STANDING   Capital City Service
WHICH WILL
NOT HELP YOU
OR HER OR   Marabou Storks
SANDY OR
BERNARD BUT IT IS STILL AN URGE YOU HAVE, FUTILE
URGE TO MAKE SENSE OF THIS FUCKING CRAZY SHITE
YOU'RE INVOLVED IN THIS TROPICAL LAND THIS
COLONISED NATION OF YOUR DISEASE MIND
Africa, my Africa . . .

Why no death
why only in competence
why when you purchase the manual
is it that you still can't do it right
in our flat Dorie, mind the time I fucked up
putting up the shelves
I had the manual and all the right tools then

IT WON'T HURT, ROY, YOUR UNCLE
GORDON WOULD NEVER HURT YOU
JUST LIE STILL PERFECTLY STILL NOW
ROY, OR THERE WILL BE BIG TROUBLE
WHEN YOUR DAD HEARS ABOUT THIS
SHUT UP YOU LITTLE BASTARD I'M
WARNING YOU SHUT THE FUCK UP
THAT'S BETTER THAT'S BETTER
THERE THERE THERE

k.d.

k.d. lang has a lot to answer for, I know because I'm living with her. I mean I'm not talking just fan club stuff here, or even hairstyles. I'm talking k.d. all over the fuckin' place and she's turning into one son of a bitch. I should have known when I came home and she was sitting cross-legged, which she never does normally on account of her back, zoom lens six inches from the telly screen, completely oblivious to anything else. I drew breath and said, 'What do you think you're doing?'

She never answered, just kept very still zooming in and out, in and out at that bloody k.d. lang video, then click. 'That would have been perfect but for you,' she said.

That was all. Got up, with a bit of difficulty, and went out the back. No explanation. I said to myself, Tracey, now don't overreact. It's coming up to the anniversary of her mother's death and we all know what that can mean. Well, there was no tea made, although it was one of the days she doesn't work. I wouldn't mind for me, but it's the kids. All they've had all day is a plate of chips and a custard doughnut. She says they should eat a proper school meal then, and I say that is a proper school meal. It's been that way since they privatised. She doesn't listen. But of course it never ends there. Next thing you know,

51

Frank's got wind that we're not feeding them properly. It's Darren that does it, he knows how to get his dad round his little finger. He only sees them once a fortnight, so out they go for a pizza, or a McDonald's.

'Now look here, Tracey,' he'll say when he brings them back, 'I only agreed to you two having them on certain conditions, and feeding 'em right is one of 'em.' Hasn't got a clue.

'Oh,' I say, 'and when's the last time you clothed them? Do you know how much a pair of trainers cost?'

'You know I'm not working, Trace but I'd do a darn sight better for them than you if I was.'

He always flings this over his shoulder as he's going down the front path, and he knows I won't scream at him out there because of the neighbours. They talk enough about us as it is.

So this time, it being near the anniversary an' all, I follows her out the back. She's out there on one of her raised beds, as she calls them, pulling stuff up for all she's worth. I sit down at a reasonable distance – she doesn't like her space being cramped does our Linda – and say as lovingly as I can, 'Look, Lynn, I don't mind you taking pictures of the telly, but we've got to get our priorities right.'

Well, I've hardly finished me sentence and she's on her feet, flinging green stuff everywhere, shouting, 'Priorities! Priorities, is it. *You* want *us* to get *our* priorities right. Get our fucking priorities right. Priorities need putting right, she says. Priorities, priorities, priorities. Whose fucking priorities! Well, I'll give you *my* fucking priorities. Watch this.'

And she marches into the house and starts flinging all her things out of the wardrobe onto the landing. Half of it sticks to the banister on the way down the stairs. 'I'm moving into the shed,' she's bawling, 'but I'll not relegate on me duties.'

I thought, fuck, she's lost it, and I thought about phoning her brother, but he'd just say what do you expect when she's living with a dyke. It would drive anybody into a shed. So I said nothing and did nothing. Just stood at the bottom of the stairs while she carted all her stuff out the back. Then in she comes, pushes past me into the kitchen, picks up a saucepan, bang it goes on the stove.

'Right,' she says, 'is it going to be quarter-inch, half-inch or one-inch burgers?'

I was just about to say, Linda, we have no burgers, but she interrupted with, '. . . or does the alternative family want fish fingers and beans, or spaghetti hoops, alphabet pasta, potato waffles and spice-coated chips, French bread pizza and . . .'

By this time she's dancing round the kitchen singing it to that song out of *The Sound of Music*. The kids are at the door gobsmacked, but Darren manages to pipe up, 'Spicy-coated chips, please.'

This stops her in her tracks. She pulls open the freezer door, the one me mam bought us saying that's the nearest you'll get to a wedding present, and flings the floppy packet on the table. 'Ger yer own then!' she snarls and shoots out the door.

The kids have stopped crying now. The spicy chips went down well, despite the introduction they were given. They're on that play station thing now, shooting every foreign agent in sight. She's up there. I can see the torch through the shed window. I think she wouldn't do this but for the good weather, but I'm not so sure. So I'll go up with a bottle of that Chardonnay stuff she likes and two glasses. We're supposed to be saving it for Christmas, but there'll be no Christmas at this rate.

'How you doing, kid?' I say at the shed door.

I must admit she's got it nice. Camping roll's out, and she's found that ripped bean-bag for a pillow, but she's not hung her clothes up yet. She looks up at me and bursts into tears. So I sneak in beside her and put me arm around her, very slow like. She's sobbing and saying, 'What does it all mean?'

At first I'm thinking she means the spicy-coated chips and then I realise she's on about something else.

'I mean,' she keeps saying, 'what does it all mean?'

And I keep quiet because I'm not sure meself. Then she says, 'Bernice and Joan have split up.' Well, I'm shocked.

'Bernice and Joan?' I say. 'Never.'

She looks at me, tears all down her face and her nose is running snotters. She wipes it with her sleeve, nodding.

'Well, who'd believe it?' I say.

So we sit in the quiet for a while, and she says, 'Are we all right, you know, together?'

And I pull her to me right close and say, 'As right as we'll ever be kid, as right as we'll ever be.'

from

the learning of paul o'neill

GRAEME WOOLASTON
GRAEME WOOLASTON

Paul had posted off the contact ad during his second week in Eassord. He had always intended to do this once he was in Scotland; it was the obvious way to meet gay contacts when, without transport, he had no easy access to the bars of Edinburgh and Glasgow. It was also the first time since Steve's death that he had made a conscious attempt to find new partners. In his last year in Brighton he had had sex only once, with a man he picked up almost by accident at a party and afterwards 'forgot' to ring again.

He knew before he began to draft the ad that he would orient it towards SM. The inclination had always been part of his sexuality, but not only had he not practised it during his years with Steve, he hadn't even admitted its existence to him. Now, a new inhabitant of his old country, he didn't want any kind of emotionally complicated relationship. Indeed, he didn't want to be 'in love' again ever. Love, he had decided months before, was in his past, with Steve. So, if sex alone was the object, it might as well be gratifyingly sensual sex. He soon found the right, familiar form of words which would signal to those in the know what he meant. He gave his geographical location simply as 'central Scotland', and was therefore delighted to find that by far the most interesting reply was from a man who lived barely ten miles away, in a village to the north of Eassord.

This was where Bob drove him early in the evening. His house was on the edge of the village: modern, detached, with a large, well-kept garden. Paul put down his bag with his gear in the sitting-room and went to the back window. The evening was light and clear; beyond Bob's garden, which was on a descending slope, he could see for 20 miles, to the familiar peaks of the Grampians. From this direction the conical shape of Ben Lomond, almost symmetrical except for what looked like a chunk bitten out of the top of it, dominated the range.

'You have a fantastic view,' Paul remarked as Bob came into the room behind him.

'You said that the last time.'

Paul turned, smiling.

'God, am I getting boring already?'

Bob laughed.

'No, of course not.' He went to a well-stocked drinks cabinet. 'What's your anaesthetic?' he asked.

They sat in facing armchairs. Paul's 'anaesthetic' was an Islay malt, diluted slightly with Scottish mineral water. While he and Bob chatted, as yet keeping off the subject which had brought them together, Paul looked round the room. Everything spoke of prosperity greater than just that of a successful accountant. He knew from their first meeting that Bob had attended a fee-paying school in Glasgow, and he assumed that family money had contributed to the furniture, the décor, the paintings on the walls – mostly bright abstracts, contrasting with the cream and white which dominated the room's colour scheme.

Bob talked about his work. He was short, lean and, apart from the fact that his hair was starting to thin, which he disguised by keeping it cut short, he looked younger than his years. Paul knew from their first encounter that he had well-shaped muscles, the fruit of a deliberate project of work-outs. As a result he could wear leather well; but at present he was still in the trousers of his working suit, and a collar and tie. The formality didn't surprise Paul. In due course it would fit into the context of what they were going to do, as would his own T-shirt and jeans.

'And what have you been up to since I saw you last?' Bob asked.

'Not a lot. Working.'

'Still planning a new book?'

Paul grinned.

'I'm *always* planning a new book. Yes, I'm deep in plotting, all that sort of thing.'

Bob nodded.

'What's it going to be about, this book?'

Paul disliked talking about his writing, except with close friends.

'Oh – much the same as the ones before it.'

Bob nodded again, and shifted in his chair.

'And what have you been up to that needs correction?'

Paul's stomach tensed slightly. So, the business of the evening had begun. He put down his glass.

'Precious little, I'm afraid.'

'Well, that's hardly satisfactory, is it?'

They looked at each other. This was the stage in any SM session which Paul found the most difficult to negotiate: the transition from normal conversation into a scenario, into the beginning of role-playing. He felt more acutely self-conscious at this point than at any time later; also, invariably, he had a strong urge to call a halt immediately. Though he knew that throughout all that was going to happen he would be able to stop it if it became too much for him, nonetheless he was beginning to be afraid. But his fear was also the beginning of his pleasure. He needed to be scared, he needed to have the challenge to surmount.

'You're very scruffy,' Bob said.

Paul glanced down at himself.

'What do you mean,' Bob went on, 'by turning up in jeans?'

'They're very smart jeans,' Paul countered.

Bob raised his eyebrows.

'That sounded cheeky to me, O'Neill. Definitely cheeky.'

Paul said nothing. The switch to the use of his surname indicated that the scene had begun in earnest.

'Stand up, O'Neill,' said Bob.

Paul hesitated for a moment, then stood up. This was the most crucial step of all out of normality and into SM. He had surrendered control over his body; it was beginning to do what someone else told it to do.

'I don't think your jeans are so smart,' Bob went on, 'that they wouldn't be improved by a little dusting. I think six of the best is in order, don't you, O'Neill?'

Again Paul hesitated before he said simply: 'Yes, sir.'

His hesitation hadn't been acted. He genuinely found it extremely difficult, until he became used to it again, to call anyone 'sir'. He could enjoy being addressed by his surname, to place him in a submissive role; it was much harder for him to speak in turn as if acknowledging a superior.

'Good,' Bob said. 'Go and put one of those dining chairs into the middle of the room there.'

As Paul did so, Bob stood up. When the chair was in place he said: 'Stand behind it.'

Paul got into position.

'Now stay there,' Bob said, and went out of the room.

He took longer to return than was necessary; he had simply crossed the hall into another room. Paul knew he was being made to wait, he was being given time to get nervous.

When Bob re-entered the room he had a cane in his hands. He drew the curtains over the windows before walking across to stand behind Paul. He just said: 'Bend over.'

Paul bent, grasping the front legs of the chair for support.

Bob gave him six strokes. They stung, each hurting for a few seconds before the next followed. But they were nothing like 'six of the best', nor were they meant to be; they were intended just to stimulate Paul at the beginning of the session. When he straightened up he smarted to an extent which was only moderately unpleasant.

Bob stood in front of him and looked at him.

'I have a feeling, O'Neill,' he said, 'that perhaps that caning wasn't very effective.'

Paul understood what he was asking.

'It did hurt a bit, sir.'

'Only "a bit", eh? Well, that's hardly satisfactory, is it?' Paul said nothing. 'I think we'd better give you another six, without the benefit of your jeans to protect you this time. Eh?'

'Yes, sir,' Paul said quietly.

'Good. Strip to your underpants.'

Paul threw his shirt and jeans over the back of the sofa and turned to face Bob in just his white y–fronts. At times like these he was grateful that he had aged so little he still had the hairless chest and slim physique of a teenager. Bob flexed the cane between his hands and studied him. With a thrill of satisfaction, Paul saw in his eyes his appreciation of the body in front of him.

'Right, O'Neill. Now you're much more appropriately dressed to be taught a lesson. Bend over again.'

When Paul bent he took a firmer hold of the chair's legs than before, bracing himself for the first real pain of the encounter. This time the caning made him wince and gasp, though he knew that Bob was still holding back and not inflicting the hurt he could have done.

Even so, when he stood up his backside stung sharply and at once he wanted to rub it, but Bob said: 'Stand to attention, O'Neill. Hands by your side. Straighten your shoulders.'

Paul complied. Bob laid his cane on the table, came back, and began to caress Paul's buttocks. At the touch Paul started to harden.

'Yes,' Bob said, 'your arse is beginning to warm up, O'Neill.' He stepped away and gently tugged down Paul's pants at the back – taking care, Paul noticed, not to reveal him at the front; it was too early in the scene for that. 'Yes,' Bob said again, 'your arse is nicely reddened. Smarting, is it, O'Neill?'

'Yes, sir.'

Bob began to caress him again. 'But you deserve much more, don't you, O'Neill?'

There was an almost bizarre contrast between the harshness of what Bob was saying and the gentleness with which his hands were moving: his touch was that of an admirer, even a lover, and it was keeping Paul hard.

'Yes, sir.'

After a moment Bob softly pulled Paul's pants back up again.

'Very well. For the time being you can stand like this and smart. But keep firmly to attention or you'll find yourself smarting a lot more.'

He went over to his chair, sat down, and resumed his unfinished gin and tonic, leaving Paul in the middle of the room. Paul didn't object; this was a way of continuing the scene, maintaining his loss of control over his body to Bob, while giving him time to recover from his first canings. The stinging was already fading rapidly.

After a minute Bob stood up, opened a drawer in a bureau in the corner, and pulled out an object which Paul recognised from last time. It was a long, two-tailed belt of the type which until two years previously had been used in Scottish schools; the kind of belt with which Paul himself had been strapped as a schoolboy. Bob came over with it and stood in front of him.

'I remember that the last time you were here you preferred to have your arse tanned with this belt rather than your hands warmed. Isn't that so, O'Neill?'

'Yes, sir.'

'Well, I'm going to give you a word of warning. If at any time tonight you present yourself in front of me in the wrong kit I won't give you any choice about holding out your hands. Do you understand?'

Paul understood perfectly.

'Yes, sir.'

'Good. Now get all this clutter out of here, go across the hall, and come back in white PE shorts. I think it's time we put you through some exercises. You may relax.'

Paul stood easy, and turned. He took his things and crossed to the room, a small study, where Bob had gone earlier. Being required to change like this out of Bob's sight wasn't, he knew, because of some strange prudery; it was so that when he finally was stripped naked in front of Bob it would be part of the scene.

He took off his underpants and selected from his bag the white cotton PE shorts Bob wanted him to wear. He knew what was going to happen when he went back. Bob's invasion of control over his body would be extended as he ordered him to do press-ups and sit-ups; he would take the role, which to Paul's amusement seemed to come naturally to him, of an impatient and scornful PE master, and then either cane or strap him through his shorts. By now he had fully recovered from his first canings, and could face another.

But as he was about to go out into the hall again he stopped and thought. He knew exactly why he had declined, last time, to let Bob belt him on the hands. It was one thing to engage in adult play-acting – until his first SM experience in London he had never so much as seen a cane – but it was quite another to choose to relive his real schoolboy punishments. Bob was the first partner he had had with whom the possibility even arose; the people he knew in England had no interest in what happened in Scottish schools.

Paul went back to his open bag. Bob had skilfully worked into the scene a signal whereby he could shape its progress. He pulled out a pair of red football shorts. If he put them on now, and so appeared in front of Bob in the 'wrong kit', he would be replicating exactly that morning when Maclaren belted him for not having his swimming-trunks.

Slowly Paul took off his white shorts. Still he hesitated. But why not? After all, he was back in Scotland, where he had taken the belt when he was just a kid. Was he going to be more of a coward now? In an abrupt rush of decision he pulled on the red shorts, turned, and headed back to Bob's sitting-room.

When everything was over, Paul, in his underpants, stood by the window looking across the view to the mountains. It was still broad daylight. Through all his years in England he had never ceased to miss these long, clear evenings of a Scottish June. Now he was home again, to enjoy them. He sipped from a glass of chilled white wine as he listened to jazz playing quietly on Bob's stereo.

He felt profoundly relaxed. And yet part of his mind contemplated what he had done in the last two hours with astonishment and intellectual unease. When he arrived he had expected the evening to be similar to the first he had spent with Bob; but it had developed into something much heavier. Not for many years had he explored so far down this by-lane of his psychology, had surrendered so completely to the compulsion to let humiliation and pain lead him to the release of satisfaction, like a sunburst after a storm, at their end.

Bob came over to him. He was in the black leather jeans and white T-shirt he had worn for their final session. He touched Paul on the shoulder: 'Are you all right?'

Paul turned, smiling.

'Yes, fine.'

'I didn't go too far at the end, did I?'

Paul shook his head. 'No, you didn't, don't worry.'

'I was wondering, perhaps . . .'

Paul repeated: 'Don't worry! I'd have stopped you if I really wanted to.'

'Well, if you're sure . . . Shall we sit down?' Suddenly he grinned. '*Can* you sit down?'

Paul laughed as he crossed the room.

'Of course I can! But do you think I should put on some more clothes?'

'Are you cold?' Paul shook his head. 'Then don't, please. You look nice as you are.' They sat side by side on the sofa. 'I can't tell you,' Bob went on, 'what a pleasant change it is to meet a young man who wears decent underpants, and not those awful boxer shorts.'

Paul laughed again, partly at the compliment to his age: 'Thanks.'

He put down his glass and looked at his hands.

'It's a long time since I saw *that* on my palms,' he remarked. The imprints of Bob's belt were pale blue outlines.

'Honestly,' Bob said, 'I'm a brute. You shouldn't let me do things like that to you.'

'Stop worrying about it!'

They had had two sessions, with a break between them for more drinks and to discuss how the second should proceed. For it Bob changed into his T-shirt and leather jeans and treated Paul, who was again in shorts, like a trainee on punishment drill. Periods of exercise alternated with times when Paul had to stand strictly to attention. When Bob belted him in the second session he didn't hold back, as he had done before, on what he was doing; the strokes hurt with all the pain Paul remembered from his schooldays.

As the last part of the scene Bob put a cushion over the back of a chair. When Paul bent over it Bob handcuffed each of his wrists to the chair legs. Though the position wasn't uncomfortable in itself, Paul was genuinely unable to move; but he had agreed beforehand to this.

Bob stood behind him: 'Get your legs apart, O'Neill. Wider yet. I want your shorts stretched as tight as a drumskin. Keep going.' Paul complied. 'Okay.' He went to an armchair and sat down. 'In a few minutes I'm going to teach you one final lesson. While I relax you can think about what your arse has got coming to it.' He picked up his drink.

Paul made no effort to break off the scene. There was an element of genuine humiliation in the helplessness with which he was bound, as there had been every time he had bent over or held out his hands or dropped to the floor to do press-ups. But he knew he wanted it, he wanted for a short time in his well-controlled life to be under the control of someone else, however much he retained the final power to halt the arrangement if he had to.

At last Bob stood up.

'Okay, O'Neill.' He picked up his belt. 'It's time to give the seat of your pants a sound dusting.' He struck Paul once. 'If you've the balls to take it, that is. Well, O'Neill? Are you going to be a man, or do you want me to let you off?'

Paul said quietly: 'No, sir.'

'Very well, then.' He ran his hand over Paul's buttocks: 'Not going to be much use to you now, these tight little shorts, are they?'

'No, sir.'

The beating was the only one of the session which caused Paul any substantial distress. Bob's belt was heavy, and he laid it on with some force. Gradually Paul came closer and closer to asking him to stop; but as each successive shock of pain faded again his pride intensified that he was keeping silent. By the end he was hard.

Bob stepped back.

'Well, O'Neill. I take it you won't be in a hurry for a repeat of that?'

'No, sir.'

Bob tugged down Paul's shorts to mid-thigh. He stroked Paul's buttocks. 'A hot little arse.' After a moment he added: 'You've got a very neat pair of buns, O'Neill.'

Slightly startled, Paul said, 'Thank you, sir.'

'But you took that very bravely.'

Paul realised the compliment, strange as it was, was genuine. He repeated: 'Thank you, sir.'

Abruptly Bob's voice was different.

'Paul, are you okay?'

Paul was taken by surprise by the suddenness with which Bob had ended the scene. He twisted round: 'Yes, I'm fine.'

'You aren't too sore?'

'No worse than I expected. I'm more numb than sore.'

Bob put the belt down.

'Are you comfortable, or could you manage to stay like that for another minute or two?'

'Yes, I could. Why?'

'Because if I don't bring myself off soon, I'm going to burst my pants.'

Paul smiled. Bob lay on the floor behind him and unzipped

himself. Paul listened as he began to masturbate: already quickly, and with rapid breaths. He paused once: 'Christ, Paul, but you've got a lovely arse, you really have.'

'Thanks,' Paul said, smiling again.

Bob's breathing grew faster and faster till he came with a loud groan, and then lay, his breathing returning to normal, till he said: 'Thanks, Paul. Thanks.'

He stood up and went to the table, cleaned himself with a tissue, and zipped his trousers. He turned round and ruffled Paul's hair: 'You really are brave, you know. I don't think I could have taken that last hiding.'

Paul didn't know how to reply. Bob knelt in front of him, unlocking the cuffs. Paul straightened up, his back aching slightly from his having been bent over: 'I'm stiff in all the wrong places,' he said with a brief grin at the age of the joke as he rid himself of the encumbering shorts.

Bob stood in front of him: 'Put your wrists together and let me cuff you again.'

Paul was startled.

'Why?'

'Because I'd like to bring you off myself. May I?'

Paul had never been jerked off while his own hands were bound. Immediately the idea excited him: 'Okay.'

Bob handcuffed him and then, standing behind him, took him in his arms and began to finger his cock. Paul hardened: 'But I'll come on your carpet,' he said.

'That doesn't matter.'

Bob began to masturbate him. Within seconds Paul surrendered to the pleasure of being embraced by this man who had hurt him so much; he felt Bob's torso against his back, the leather rubbing against his thighs and buttocks: 'Harder!' he urged, and after a minute, 'Quicker!' – then he arched back and cried out as Bob's fingers pumped wave after wave of orgasm down his cock; he cried out again as the sensations faded and he realised that not for a long time had the pleasure gone so deep or suffused so far through his whole body.

Bob held him, kissing his back, till Paul said quietly: 'Thanks, Bob.'

Bob let him go. He fetched a tissue across: 'Let me dry you,' he said.

The touch of Bob's hands on his cock and over his belly was as tender as a nurse's. Paul, looking down, smiled.

Bob freed him again from the cuffs: 'If you like, you can go upstairs and have a bath. By the time you get back I'll have fixed up some music and drinks for us.'

The next morning Bob, dressed again as an accountant, dropped Paul off in Alnebrig on his way to work. As Paul entered the house he met Anne, who started to laugh.

'I see coming back to Scotland hasn't improved your morals.'

Paul was embarrassed.

'We just – we just sat up late talking about books.'

'Of course you did. What sort of books?'

Paul grinned.

'Leather-bound ones.'

'I see! I'm not sure I want to know any more.'

'Don't worry,' Paul said as he turned towards the staircase to the flat. He grinned again. 'Bob's trying to make a good boy of me.'

After breakfast he lay on his bed, stripped from the waist down, and began lazily to masturbate. His thoughts wandered over the previous evening. Though the memories excited him, and he knew they would provide food for his fantasies for several days, the intellectual unease which had troubled him when he stood by Bob's window returned. Could it be right, could it be justifiable, to gratify such a passion for pain? He was ready with a defence: that it was preferable by far to grant such a passion its proper outlet in consensual sex, than to vent it in cruelties in the real world. But the doubts persisted. A dark passion was a dark passion, however much it had to be indulged from time to time to keep it under control. And could he deny that somewhere, in some very important part of his psyche, he was stuck in adolescence? Wasn't he just giving an adult gloss to the schoolboy desire to prove he could 'take it'?

He looked at his hands. The marks of Bob's belt were still clear, if faint. Dear God, to have done that again: to have stood with his hands out for the belt. But it had been necessary. It had been necessary, now he was back in the town of his childhood, not just to act out a fantasy, but to recreate what had happened in reality.

JOSEPH MILLS

the sons of cary elder

Los Gorbals, November 2019

There was nobody on the landing. And there was nobody in the store room. The store room had not been repaired yet: the Yale lock was still dangling by one rusty nail two weeks after the door had last been kicked in. But there was nobody in the store room. There was nobody sleeping something off, waiting to rob the flats when the coast was clear, waiting to jump out and mug one of the tenants. Daniel couldn't think of any other reason why anybody would want to break into a four by six mucky, empty store room on the 21st floor of a dingy high-rise flat. And then break in again when the door had been nailed back by the concierge.

Someone had removed the half-empty can of super-lager that had been sitting there for the last three days and put a large cube of air freshener in its place. Daniel felt slightly ashamed that he hadn't removed the can of lager himself. But then none of the other tenants had until now. He would have put it down the chute if it was his turn to mop the landing. Anyway, for all he knew it could have belonged to one of the neighbours. Still, the air freshener was nice: at least one other tenant cared.

Daniel returned to his flat, shut and bolted the door, turned three locks and slipped a small metal wedge into the tiny space between floor and door. That, he told himself every time he did it, could be the last line of defence if anybody managed to break through all the locks. That little piece of metal could detain them for those vital extra seconds until a neighbour or concierge arrived or Daniel woke up, if the ultimate nightmare happened and they came in the night. Although what difference his being awake would make he couldn't imagine.

After he'd done all the locking he put his ear to the door and listened for five minutes. There was another, even smaller store room on the landing which didn't seem to have been interfered with but someone might have gotten a key from somewhere, may have been silently waiting there for some time. Maybe the concierges were in cahoots with the criminals and were giving out keys.

Just as he'd decided the noise that had awoken him was probably only the rumblings of the lift again he noticed a card lying flat against the door. It had obviously slid down from the letterbox and stuck there that morning; he just hadn't noticed it. He hadn't been out all day so the hall light hadn't been lit and left on while he was away to make it look as though someone was in. There was no need to imagine that anybody had been in the house while he slept or even while he had just been on the landing. Only another tenant could have done that and he would had have to have been lightning quick and outer-space silent. There was no need to fear that someone was in the house right now. Why would anybody leave a note at the door then hide in a cupboard?

He picked the card up and then dropped it. His hands weren't shaking but they were stiff and jerky, like his neck. It landed face up. It was from John Sinclair, one of his brothers' fathers.

'Just dropped this off while you were out.'

John always left cards without knocking then pretended Daniel had been out, so he knew he hadn't slept through that, but it worried him that he hadn't heard the card coming through the letterbox –

usually he could hear traffic start on the West Side, even in his sleep.

'We haven't seen you in months, thought it was because we were old fogeys and all that, but even Jordan says he hasn't heard from you. Hey! Even NONies have to communicate sometimes.'

Father and Father and Son

Jordan, Daniel's half-brother, obviously wasn't shown this before it was delivered or he would have told John that those who had decided against or were too poor for the Internet and all that went with it – Not On Net – hated being called NONies. It was ironic: John, with his videophones, faxes and computers in every room, was just as out of touch as Daniel was. The idea that being connected to 90 per cent of the human race online meant that you were in tune with everything going on was one of the greatest myths of the 21st century.

He was annoyed at John for sneaking up there and leaving that card. He had told them all so often how frightening it was to come in and find strange stuff on the floor. He decided he would have the letterbox nailed shut like the other tenants. All his mail was collected at the mail point in town anyway. The postman had been exterminated by e-mail, and those strange creatures who shunned or couldn't afford electronic letters had to visit the nearest point periodically to find out if anybody still loved them. It was the fact that this block of flats had been one of the few remaining with letterboxes that had attracted Daniel when he left home and was looking for somewhere to stay.

There was no need, but he quickly examined every cupboard in the flat for intruders, then put the heater on in the bathroom and crept back under the covers for an hour until the room and the immerser were hot enough for a bath.

He looked again at the card: it was gold rimmed, every word a different colour. People used printed material so infrequently that when they did they turned into children with their electronic paint boxes. He decided he wouldn't visit John and his partner Will, even though Will – the replacement for Daniel's own father when he and

John split up – was a good laugh and managed to find clever ways of giving him economic aid which Daniel could accept with pride intact. Anyway, their son Jordan, although just over 18 and legally free to live anywhere, would almost certainly be there. Amazing how, now that they could transport their 3-D images across the world, people were clinging together more and more. Every week a new Net café/pub/workshop opened up even though there was no need for face-to-face contact and all communication could be conducted online. Why shouldn't they leave each other alone? More to the point, why couldn't they leave Daniel alone? Hardly a week went by without one of the relatives trying to coax him out. The worst were the ones he had least connection to. Like Kyle, his eldest half-brother.

Father and Mother and Son
He had barely known Kyle: the mother had taken him out of the country with her after the divorce, when he was barely eight. And yet for 13 years he had been writing letters and sending cards. A few months ago Daniel had actually received a *hand-written* birthday card from Kyle. Quite clever too: a picture of his block of flats and the lyrics to The Specials' 'Ghost Town' superimposed over it in electric blue.

'Happy 18th. In case you don't get it: this was number one exactly 20 years before the day you were born. A lot has changed in 38 years, Daniel.'

Yes, Kyle, very impressive. Joined-up writing. Whatever next? Daniel used the anger-energy from that memory to get him through the bath (neither the water nor the room temperature was nearly warm enough) and out the door (after packing away irreplaceables in the hidey-holes he'd created). He picked up some headache pills from the Chinese hypermarket, noted that beans were still at giveaway prices, although still subject to the 'No more than five items per person' rule. Daniel lived on the white label stuff they sold in the hypermarkets. If they ever closed down, as the government intended, his own economy would collapse. Children and teens were collecting their various maintenance drugs – heroin, marijuana, valium – from the chemist, shuffling in, head down in silence, skipping out with smiles for everyone. Oldies still got by on alcohol.

Daniel decided to go to Adam's.

Father and Self and Son
Next to his father, Adam was his 'nearest'. Given that terms such as father had become so ambiguous, new labels had evolved. His half-brothers Kyle and Jordan were his 'furthest' since they only shared his father's genes. His 'father' Cary, the body he was cloned from, was his nearest, being identical genealogically speaking. Adam was somewhere in between, having been produced with DNA from two different sperms from his father. Daniel was a clone of Cary, but Adam was a near clone and only a month older than Daniel, so they could have been more alike than 'father' and son. Except that they were brought up in totally different environments and had turned out totally differently.

Daniel was going to Adam's that day mainly to get something to eat. He had calculated that he would only be able to smoke till benefit day if he skipped three meals – or ate one big one for free.

The artificial heat on the West Side began to drain his energy five minutes after he'd crossed the border. As soon as he rang the doorbell the dogs started barking. He heard ornaments avalanche off the surfaces they were piled high on as the cats trampolined all over the place, avoiding the dogs. Angela, Adam's girlfriend, let him in then ran past to capture two small dogs and a big fat cat. Daniel made his way over to the sofa and attempted to take his shoes off while the dogs fought over his laces. After all the animals had been patted and praised and licked his face to their satisfaction he settled down.

'Didn't you get our birthday card?' Angela asked.

'Oh, yes. Safe and sound.'

'I don't trust that post nonsense. If only you'd let us give you one small terminal –'

'We're making chilli if that's all right.'

They had the usual tiresome three-way conversation. Adam and he talked about music and films until Angela became jealous and competitive and he talked with her about politics until it was back to Adam and soap star gossip. Daniel found the competitiveness as childish as the constant one-upmanship – for every dog she had cloned, he had cloned two cats.

And if they drank it was worse. Angela would start praising Daniel and then Cary at Adam's expense. This would begin with her staring at them when they were discussing something she felt left out of, comparing their looks, which would have been identical if Adam wasn't a hippy and Daniel a skinhead. They had each conformed to the stereotypes of their own side of town. Daniel looked down on Adam's style and knew that the opposite was true.

Whenever Adam and Angela got into some Net gossip Daniel could not contribute to, he would glance around the electronic clutter of the room, the multiple screens chattering away to each other, the cameras and microphones recording and relaying their every word and gesture, trying again to work out whether his claustrophobia and disdain was genetic or environmental. But that was impossible. So much for the experiments.

The rules of reproduction were that nobody could produce children in the same way twice. With complete global capitalism efficiency was all: everything had to be categorised and costed; the more data available on consumers' likely moods and appetites the more efficient and profitable companies and governments would be. So every child, which would be consuming vast amounts of ever scarcer resources, had to be an experiment, an evolution. If you had one heterosexually the next had to be produced homosexually or through cloning or parthenogenesis or any of the other methods they had come up with. They could scoop out the genetic material from an egg and put almost any mixture in its place now. No parent was allowed more than one child at home – until it was 18 and of little use to the experiments. The birth rate dropped because of this rule but not as much as had been supposed: couples still wanted copies or amalgamations of themselves, even if they only kept in touch electronically. Daniel had been assigned to the East Side with well-meaning working-class parents who lost interest in him pretty quickly and left him to his own devices. Adam was brought up on the West Side by a virtual reality programmer and an exercise video consultant. And what had that proved?

Father and Clone
Daniel had turned out gay because he was the clone of a gay man. Adam and the other three brothers were straight because most children of gay fathers are straight, even two gay fathers.

'So what's all the fuss about?' Angela would say, well down the brandy bottle, at the patronising stage. It had been a gay man who had made the breakthrough in human cloning in 2001, although he never told the world until five years later when his and his friends' clones and same-sex fathered and mothered children were cleared of any abnormalities after years of rigorous testing.

Some people – those unable to produce their own children – were grateful. Most weren't. New laws were greased through parliament slicker than shite on a shiny boot. Gays were still kept in the minority through law and many straights were clamouring for an end to cloning to keep things that way since, despite stepping up the search, they still hadn't found that elusive gay gene. They thought they'd almost proved that sexuality was genetic: gay clones had been brought up in every possible environment and, given the choice, no more or less crossed sexual boundaries than had done so before. But then they found that straight boy clones, brought up on all-male islands, were fucking each other like rabbits the moment they hit puberty. Other results were equally predictable. Half the children stayed in the environment they were born in, like Daniel, the others crossed the border as soon as they turned 18.

'Nothing's really changed,' Angela said.

But she didn't know, as Daniel did, that some people were planning on making things change. She didn't know about the little gang that had formed in reaction to the laws. The little rich, powerful and busy gang.

'Are you coming for the new year celebrations?'

'I'm a bit wary of leaving the flat empty at such a time.'

'You don't *have* to stay in that awful place now. You're more than welcome here.'

'I'll write and let you know.'

The nearest mail point was on the wrong side of the border: they all knew this was Daniel's way of saying 'No way'.

He returned to the East Side, ears still buzzing with the chattering electronic voices, satisfied once more that his way was best. As he entered the flat he didn't feel the trepidation he usually did on returning home after a long spell away: Leo was coming round that night. The only thing Daniel would admit to in the way of dissatisfaction was that, yes, maybe if you were alone, then the West Side with its contact, comfort and security was best. But he wasn't alone and he preferred romantic poverty with Leo to sharing him with the Networld.

Leo was full of news about The Plan. They both changed their minds about The Plan daily. When Daniel was 15 and his father, Cary, first introduced him to the collective, he was as committed as all the other militant gays – furious that they were still forced to be a minority, furious that the goalposts had been moved when the percentage of gays grew alarmingly as more of them went in for cloning than straights.

'They want to find a gay gene so straights can produce only more straights,' Cary had argued, 'but we aren't allowed the same privilege.'

Cary spoke with all the conviction of the Born Again: even gays who fathered homosexually were somewhat frowned upon as selfish, given the probability of adding to the hetero numbers, but Cary had coupled with a woman, the ultimate crime.

'Got there in the end, though, didn't I?' he would say, giving Daniel's jet-black crew-cut – identical to his own except in colour – a fatherly rub. The Plan had begun benevolently enough: it occurred to gays that it was possible, if they could convince enough rich and high-placed homos, to create a completely gay space for themselves, with cloning the only means of reproduction allowed to keep the space purely gay. Some women – not all gay – had already started their own women-only colonies. But The Plan quickly became more ambitious and confrontational: they could have a wholly gay community. It was their due. The whackier evangelists even pointed out that if they gained control of The Bomb, they could, in a generation, wipe all heteros off the face of the earth. Daniel and Leo went over it all again that night, wrapped up by the fire. Cary had scared them when he came over recently and installed some state-of-the-art anti-bugging software in Daniel's walls.

'You know, I could get lynched for this.'

'But if we leave the group we just leave. We're not going to be giving away any trade secrets.'

'You and I know that but they don't for sure.'

'It's all getting a bit too 20th-century for me.'

'Don't ever say that outside this room – and don't get complacent because of this,' he ran his hand up and down a wall. 'There are still the good old-fashioned methods of surveillance.'

Daniel and Leo decided that they would resign from the collective.

'There's too much that could go wrong with trying to keep a space completely gay,' Leo said. 'Do you have to be 100 per cent queer? Where do bisexuals go? What happens if a gay man and a lesbian have a hetero child – do we throw it in the river?'

'Or let it stay on as a frowned-upon minority?'

Daniel washed dishes, satisfied that they'd finally come to a decision. Cary would stay in the collective, he thought. Maybe Leo's and his generation was more accepting of rules they'd grown up with rather than had thrust upon them. He was just reaching for the headache pills when he heard a noise outside.

They found a tramp lying in the store room, wrapped in bin liners.

'What time is it?' he asked.

'Three a.m.,' Daniel answered automatically, startled.

'Oh, well, I'll have another half-hour then.'

The tramp turned over.

They went back to the flat and listened at the door for five minutes. Just as they were about to go to bed they heard the unmistakable tinkling of a video phone in use.

Daniel locked and bolted the door and put the metal wedge in place.

The next day he nailed up the letterbox.

JIMMY MCGOVERN

priest

Father Greg is a gay priest who has just been outed by a local rag: not in front of the altar boys screamed the headline. Having attempted suicide and been told by his bishop that 'The best way to serve God is to piss off out of my diocese', he has been exiled to the parish of grim Father Redstone, who welcomes him thus: 'Scio te penitus. Tu es pustula in corpore Christi, pustula vivens, spirans, monstrousa, iam iamque in pus et cruorem et foetorem eruptura.'

Father Greg: I'm sorry, you've lost me.

Redstone: I said, 'I know all about you. You're a boil on the body of Christ. A monstrous, living, breathing boil, about to erupt at any minute into pus and blood and stench.'

Father Greg: I think I preferred it in Latin.

Father Matthew is his only friend and ally left . . .

Father Redstone's house. Greg's bedroom. Day.
Greg standing by the window, rain lashing down. He's never been so miserable.

He sees something through the downpour . . .

Father Redstone's house. Night.
Matthew, soaked, dismounts from his bike, takes a bottle of whisky
from his saddlebag, approaches the door.

Father Redstone's house. Dining Room. Night.
Greg and Matthew have made serious inroads into the bottle of
whisky.

> *Matthew*
> You've broken a vow of celibacy.
> *Greg*
> Bollocks . . .
> *Matthew*
> You should demand to be treated the same as
> any other priest. Heterosexual, homosexual, it
> makes . . .
> *Greg*
> Utter bollocks . . .
> *Matthew*
> . . . no difference. You've broken a man-made rule,
> that's all: it's there to protect property, to keep it
> away from the widows of priests. It's there . . .
> *Greg*
> Christ was celibate . . .
> *Matthew*
> . . . for mobility of labour. No wife, no kids, so
> you can kick a priest . . .
> *Greg*
> Christ was celibate . . .
> *Matthew*
> . . . from one end of the earth to the other.
> *Greg*
> Christ was celibate. Matthew, the Church gives us
> everything: money, food, shelter, respect. And all

she asks in return is celibacy. Christ gave his *life* but all we are asked for is celibacy and we can't even manage that.

Matthew

Christ didn't ask us to be celibate. It's a man-made . . .

But Greg isn't listening . . .

Greg

Solemn vows. 'Do you solemnly swear . . .?' That's our currency, Matthew. Solemn vows. And we debase it because we can't even stick to them ourselves.

Cut to more whisky being poured . . .

Greg

Suppose you're right: celibacy's a man-made law that deserves to be broken. How do I find solace in that?

Matthew

Because that's all you've done.

Greg

Bullshit. I've made love to another man. Priest or layman . . .

Matthew

That makes no difference . . .

Greg

. . . Vow of celibacy or not, it is *evil* . . .

Matthew

It isn't. It makes no bloody difference whatsoever.

Greg

You really believe that?

Matthew
Yes.
Greg
You're lying.
Matthew
I'm not lying.
Greg
Forget the ideology, Matthew. Forget the party line. Do you really believe it? Do you feel it on the pulse? Do you feel it in here [heart]?
Matthew
Yes.
Greg
You're lying.

Cut to more whisky being poured . . .

Matthew
What's his name?
Greg
Graham.
Matthew
Do you love him?
Greg
I despise him.
Matthew
Who's lying now?
Greg
Satan comes in many forms.

Matthew can't believe he's said that. Throughout what follows he will try to get face to face with Greg. Greg will try to avoid it . . .

Matthew
This is a man who's given you his body. How dare you talk like that? In the name of God, Greg, ask yourself this . . . Look at me. [He won't.] Look at me. [He won't.] To call another human being Satan, what kind of religion is that? What kind of sick, twisted brainwash have you been through? His sole purpose in life is to tempt you into sin, is that what you're saying? You're Christ, he's just the bloody serpent, is that what you're saying, you arrogant prick?

Cut to more whisky being poured. They're utterly uninhibited now, but still coherent . . .

Greg
I *think* I love him, yes.
Matthew
You want him?
Greg
Yes.
Matthew
All the time?
Greg
A lot of the time.
Matthew
You think that's sinful?
Greg [shakes head]
Sick.
Matthew
To itch for another man, that's just 'sick'. To scratch the itch, to make love to another man, that's sinful . . .

For some reason, and it's not the booze, Greg is beginning to find this funny . . .

> *Greg*
> Yes.
> *Matthew*
> And to go on scratching, to live with another man, that's permanent sin, that's evil, that's depart-from-me-ye-cursed stuff.
> *Greg* [really amused]
> Yes.
> *Matthew*
> Is there any sense, any intellect, any common humanity in that kind of bullshit, Greg? Why are you laughing? [No response] Aids is sweeping the world, common sense says stick to one long-term partner, but the Church says no that's sinful, here's a better idea: get Aids and die, be a martyr to the faith. How *dare* they expect us to swallow that? Why are you laughing? Are you laughing at me?
> *Greg*
> Yes.

Matthew studies Greg – who laughs and laughs.

> *Matthew*
> Don't patronise me, Greg.
> *Greg* [stops laughing]
> I patronise you? I live it, Matthew. You think you can walk in here and spout some glib *Guardian*-reader crap and, bang, all's right with my world. I'm reconciled to my nature, cue uplifting music? Who's the arrogant prick now?

Matthew is lost for words now. He moves around, pushes the door shut.

> Matthew
> I want you to say Mass with me in the morning.
> In my parish.
> *Greg*
> I can't.

But the door is pushed open again – to reveal Redstone sitting just outside . . .

> *Redstone*
> I want this door left open.
> *Matthew* [angry]
> I beg your pardon?
> *Greg*
> Matthew.

Matthew looks at Greg.

> *Greg*
> He's chaperoning us.

It takes a while for this to sink in. Matthew looks at Redstone, looks at Greg, begins to giggle . . . Greg begins to giggle too . . .

Father Redstone's house. Redstone's bedroom. Night.
Redstone is sleeping. Noises from next door. Moaning, passion, unbridled sex. Redstone wakes, listens to it . . .

Father Redstone's house. Greg's bedroom. Night.
Greg and Matthew have their mouths cupped to the dividing wall and are moaning away, laughing . . . The whisky bottles are empty.

<u>Father Redstone's house. Night.</u>
Greg and Matthew are drunk, shattered, and Matthew is preparing to
mount his bike.

> *Matthew*
> You owe it to them. To challenge, to confront, to
> *teach* – that's your duty.
> *Greg*
> I can't.
> *Matthew*
> Come over tomorrow. Say mass with me.
> *Greg*
> I can't.
> *Matthew*
> Big Chief Sitting Bull wouldn't hide himself away.
> *Greg*
> He'd had reservations.

It takes a little time, yes, but Matthew *does* see the joke. He starts to
giggle again. Greg too. It takes hold of Matthew and becomes helpless
laughter.
   Greg standing at the door as Matthew, laughing, mounts his bike
and cycles drunkenly off, the bicycle wobbling madly . . .

<u>Father Redstone's house. Hall.</u>
Greg closes the door. He's alone once more. His smile fades.

<u>Father Redstone's house. Greg's bedroom. Night.</u>
Greg looking up at Christ on the cross.

> *Greg* [eventually]
> Well?

<u>Father Redstone's house. Greg's bedroom. Day.</u>
Greg pulls back the curtains. Greg is dressing in civvies. Saying over and over again a couple of Latin sentences, trying to memorise them. He seems determined . . .

<u>Father Redstone's house. Day.</u>
Greg on his bike, bulging haversack on his back. Redstone at the door.

> *Greg*
> Abi et futue te ipsum, sordide senex.

Redstone doesn't understand.

> *Greg*
> It means: 'Go and fuck yourself, you old bastard.'

Greg cycles away.

from

footsteps and witnesses

EDWIN MORGAN
EDWIN MORGAN

I was born in the West End of Glasgow, in Hyndland, in 1920. I was an only child and when I was two we moved south to Pollokshields. Later we moved to Rutherglen which is almost beyond Glasgow altogether. They were a well-doing family, church-going with a strong sense of responsibility. They were the kind of parents who watched out for your moral progress and so as an only child I grew up with a pretty strong sense of what was right and what was wrong. My mother would say – you may do something that we don't know about but there's an eye up there. I was very young and I remember looking up and imagining that eye was there. I grew up with that sense of conscience pretty strongly implanted. My father worked with a firm of iron and steel merchants and he had, I suppose, a Calvinist businessman's idea. He took charge of the accounts and was extremely hard working, extremely honest, extremely conscientious and, perhaps going along with that, nervous. My mother was the same. She had the conscientiousness. I've got this nervousness still and I'm very easily made to feel that something is right or wrong.

There were other families with boys and girls of the same age round about and so I played with them in the usual way. We were in Albert Drive and I was even a member of an awful local football team called the Albertonians. I was never any good at football but you were expected to take part in group activities of that kind. I knew in myself that really wasn't my thing and maybe especially if you are an only child you tend to be by yourself and make up your own games. I collected stamps and then quite early on I began collecting words. I had a great list of words I would go through. My father would bring home gardening catalogues and I would make a list of the names of these strange, interesting plants. I don't know what I was going to do with these things but it must have been some kind of early pointer to the fact that I was going to use words myself. That was a solitary thing. I enjoyed doing that and then I kept scrap books when I was about 11. I pasted things from newspapers and magazines into jotters and I did that for years. That is probably the kind of thing an only child would do rather than someone who grew up with brothers and sisters. My parents were very sensible and they didn't spoil me but you are, inevitably I think, the centre of their interest. It probably takes you longer to rub along with other people than you would do if you had brothers and sisters but at the same time it has its own rewards in that you develop your own individuality.

I went to the local school in Rutherglen and I was there until I was 14 when my parents thought I should sit a scholarship for Glasgow High School. The last three years of my schooling from 14 to 17 I was at Glasgow High School. The first school was a mixed school and the High School was a boys' school. I didn't like school but I did well. The subjects I enjoyed most were English and Art. I was very interested in abstract design. I used to do lots of paintings of designs that were simply patterns of different colours. There was a chance of getting an apprenticeship as a carpet designer at Templeton's carpet factory in Glasgow Green when I was about 15. Then when I took my Higher Art I almost decided to go to the School of Art in Glasgow. I was perhaps persuaded by some people that this wasn't a good idea and I went to university and took English. Even back to 11 or 12, I wrote quite a lot and I think it was the right decision to carry on with the writing rather than the painting.

I knew in myself that probably the thing I enjoyed most was writing not just poems but essays. It was the life of the imagination that attracted me in writing and I tended to enjoy writers who were writing adventure stories set in far places, exotic adventure stories like Rider Haggard or science fiction stories like Jules Verne or somebody like Jack London. Things I wrote were often adventurous or set in exotic places. One of my early poems at school was called 'The Opium Smoker'. It probably comes from various things I'd read about the Far East and I enjoyed the imaginative appeal in trying to imagine what this man's life would be like. The feeling I had was that whatever you write, it isn't enough just to describe what you see around you, there's got to be something coming from the imagination. It was mostly Romantic poetry we got at school – Keats and Tennyson and Shelley. That was the first poetry I liked and it wasn't realistic. It wasn't the kind of poetry I should have been reading as a person living in Glasgow in the '30s. We started off with 19th-century literature and hardly came forward at all. It didn't encourage you to become any kind of realist in your writing. It took me a while to understand that you could write about anything – ugly things, dirty things, painful things. It can all be written about but no one told me that at school.

I was more aware of sex at the High School than I had been at Rutherglen Academy. Perhaps because it was a boys' school there was more of it going on. More relationships of various kinds – some platonic, some not platonic. More experimentation. I was very keen on a boy who was my opposite in some ways. He was sports captain of the school and we got on very well together. I used to help him with some of his problems in classwork and I had this great admiration for his physique and we often sat together. I suppose I maybe hoped that something would come of it but nothing ever did. I became sort of sexually active when we had a school trip to Germany in 1937. We were all told to wear the kilt and that obviously led to a good deal of sexual play which we all found very enjoyable and a lot of that went on in a way which was not all that furtive. The teachers seemed to regard it as something that was a part of your teens, that you would just grow out of. There was no great hassle about it. No scandals. It was something that was pleasurable and easy-going and it wasn't something that singled me out as a monster. It wasn't taken all that seriously and so I wasn't worried about it.

There were pressures when I was at the High School to meet girls. I remember being persuaded to join the local tennis club to meet girls. Of course, I did meet girls but it never led to anything. I had a very close friendship with a girl when I was at university and when I brought her home to meet my parents they presumably thought that was going to be the answer to any problems I might have had. But these things were not much discussed and the pressure wasn't intense because there wasn't the sense that you might, as it were, go the other way. I don't think my parents were worried about that because they didn't know about it.

I went to Glasgow University when I was 17 and was signed on for an Honours English degree. I took French and various different History classes and Political Economy and Russian but English was the main thing. The fact that I took Russian was just because I had a close friend who was a Communist and was taking Russian for the political point of view. We were very close friends and I didn't want to miss him and so I went to the Russian class. He was completely straight but I was bowled over about him.

I was called up in 1940 and I registered first of all as a conscientious objector. They set up tribunals where you had to explain your case but before my tribunal came up, I had changed my mind. It's difficult knowing exactly how these things happened but I think I felt it was wrong to stand aside from what was happening. It wasn't just simply a capitalist war that the worker wouldn't support. There was an actual enemy over there. I felt that I couldn't sustain my objection to killing but I suggested a compromise to the tribunal that I would be in the army but I wouldn't have a weapon and so I couldn't actually kill anyone. Shortly after that I was drafted into the Royal Army Medical Corps (RAMC) and after training near Peebles I was sent to the Middle East. I had the whole of the war there in Egypt, Lebanon, Palestine.

My main job throughout the war was quartermaster's clerk. The quartermaster looks after all the stores, medical and non-medical, and I was his assistant. I was put into a big 600-bed hospital unit – the 42nd General Hospital. We got the casualties as they were passed down to us and we were usually quite a bit from the front. In Egypt at the time when the Germans under Rommel came right up to the gates of Alexandria, we thought then that the whole thing was going to blow up. Nothing actually happened to me and that was relatively rare. We got the result of the war, the casualties, but we were not in the midst of the fighting ourselves and that was even more true when the unit was moved to Lebanon and Palestine.

There was both a lot of very intense friendship and actual sexual activity in the Army. There were always stories of the Air Force boys being up to that kind of thing but the Army was different was what I was told. A great deal of it went on and I'm sure it had something to do with the edge of the operation, the edge of life and death. You were on that edge all the time and the fact that it was often very difficult to find the time and space for sexual activity meant that it had all the more intensity when you did find that time and space. I was a private and you felt the officers must have known something about it but perhaps turned a blind eye unless it became really scandalous. I remember coming back from the nearest local town from a film show and it was late at night when the bus got back into the barracks. I was with one or two other people looking along the line of one of the other barracks and there were two soldiers in passionate embrace and no one said anything. I never found out who they were. There was a lot of that going on all the time and it had that mixture of something dangerous and at the same time liberating. Perhaps the very unexpectedness of it was liberating.

Contact was made in different ways. Sometimes it was just sitting beside someone on a bench and a knee would be pressed. Just a small physical nudge, a physical gesture would tell you that something was going on there. Perhaps nothing was spoken at all but you understood the message and you would perhaps talk to this person later on. At other times you might desire someone who wasn't going to be interested and you had to be careful. And there were lots of things in between and that was what I remember as being strange and, in a way, very interesting. There was one chap I remember, stocky, not tall, very fair, good-looking but in an extremely masculine way and very, very hairy. We used to go to the beach and you saw almost the whole body, at times the whole body, and I found this guy extremely attractive and fascinating. It was one of those things that never actually came to the bit but somehow both of us seemed to feel that it was okay not to take it any further. Sometimes we would go back together to the tented camp from having done something in the desert. There might be 20 men standing being pressed together, being jumbled together on the back of a lorry. I remember standing behind this guy, quite clearly pressed against him and he wasn't moving away and I almost came in that position. I was damp at the end of it. He didn't object but he didn't carry it any further. That kind of half-thing, half-relationship was quite common.

I kept up writing with my Communist friend from university. He was in the Artillery and we were both in Egypt. We might have met somewhere, Cairo or Alexandria. I wrote to him and poured out my feelings and he replied with a totally negative response. We both survived and went back to university to finish our degrees and the fact that he said he couldn't carry on with me on those terms meant that I myself had different feelings for him. I had two other particularly intense relationships during the war. One was physical, the other wasn't. The physical one was just something that went on from body to body but was very full and satisfying in that sense. The other one was really a pretty intense kind of love affair with a guy who was straight but liked my company. We were stationed in Sidon in Lebanon and we used to go for long walks into the hills. I really did like him tremendously. You have to have the physical thing and yet the non-physical thing which is love has to be there too. You are very lucky if you get the two coming together. It was always individuals that I remember. There were times when three or four people might know what was going on but there was no consciousness of any gay grouping or gay solidarity.

I think that more than anything else the dropping of the atom bomb on Japan hastened the end of the war and you couldn't exactly rejoice in that as an event in history. I enjoyed being back but I found it very hard to get into civilian life. It was difficult from the point of view of having rationing and all sorts of shortages for at least five years after the end of the war, but it was not just that, the whole war had made me terribly unsettled. I only went back to university because I couldn't think what to do. The fact that I hadn't been writing during the war gave me doubts about that too. There was relief at the end of the war but also a great deal of unhappiness in feeing that I wasn't adjusting to the end of the war, in peacetime terms at all. The war years had been very unproductive from the point of view of writing. There had been very good poets in the First World War who had written well about the most appalling scenes and I couldn't understand why I couldn't do the same. It was a five-year interruption in my writing, a five-year block. In the late '40s/early '50s I was writing but not well. It was a bad time for me just because I felt I wasn't doing what I should be doing.

I got a good first at Glasgow and then there was one of those times when your life forks and you have to decide. I got the chance of a scholarship to Oxford to do a further degree or I could just go directly onto the teaching staff of the English department at Glasgow University. I chose the teaching job because I was 27 and felt that I didn't really want to do any more studying. I did go down to Oxford and thought that I wouldn't be happy there. I decided then that I was probably going to stay in Scotland even if it meant I was missing the chance of a kind of mobile university career. I wanted a job that I could do and do well and I think it was also part of a feeling about Glasgow and Scotland that I perhaps didn't have before the war. Having been away from it for such a long time I had much stronger feelings about it when I came back. I liked the idea of staying there and committing myself to Scotland, just by living there and trying to make a good job of it. It took a while to become a good teacher but eventually I got to quite enjoy the job. I was also doing quite a lot of translation and translated the Old English poem 'Beowulf'. I was taking up different languages – Italian, Spanish – and I made translations from poems in other languages. I got quite a few trips from the British Council to go to other countries to give poetry readings or lectures and I tried to learn some German before I went there. I enjoyed doing all that.

Homosexual activity was just something that happened as it happened. It wasn't something you saw as any kind of political activity. There were no clubs in the modern sense of the term. No papers or magazines. It was a very unorganised, scattered and spontaneous kind of scene. There were certain pubs but they wouldn't want to be known as gay pubs. The best known one was in West Nile Street, not very far from the city centre, called the Royal. Some of the hotels had either a bar or a lounge. The Central Hotel at Central Station was a place that people often would go to. They might meet in a pub and go to the Central Hotel for a coffee afterwards. There was a certain rhythm in what people did without it being organised and you either fell in with it or you didn't. For a while I did fall into that kind of circle although I wasn't part of what you would call a grouping. Obviously there were parties. These hotels and pubs were totally mixed in a class sense. That's always been true of Glasgow and I think it's still true today. A place like the Royal would be mixed in the sense of not everyone who was there was gay but it was predominantly gay. There were lots of married men and that was surprising to me to begin with. It seems to be a very Glasgow thing. You're in the bisexual area before you know where you are. Lots of people who would hate to be called homosexual. It's very odd – protective self-delusion. Lots of people who are absolutely straight, but . . . with a big BUT at the end of the sentence.

I suppose I was just going around feeling my way, taking part in this or that but not being very much committed until I met John Scott in 1962. I was to be very close to him for 16 years. When I met him, this was a very absorbing kind of relationship and I didn't want to go back to the scene and didn't very much do so. It was both very physical and it was a love affair. It showed me that it could happen. All through the '50s, I despaired that it would ever happen. All the physical things that happened then were very enjoyable but nevertheless they didn't lead to anything else. They didn't involve feelings. It was only when I met him that there was this merging of the two. It changed my life in so many ways. My writing just took off from the time I met him and the great doubts I had about myself as a writer in the '50s just disappeared and, touch wood, will never come back. I owe everything, in a sense, to that relationship.

He lived in Lanarkshire in a small village with a large family – a very close large family and so it was very difficult for him to break out of that. His job was there too and so we didn't actually live together. I saw him every weekend and we went on holidays together but we never lived together. I think also, as a writer, I always sensed, maybe subconsciously, that I had to be by myself to get writing. I find that if I'm with somebody in the same house or same room I can't write. I have to be alone to write. From that point of view also this relationship was always there but it left me free to do my writing. He accepted this too and it didn't worry him.

The 1960s was the period I enjoyed most – partly because of the love affair, partly because of other kinds of liberation. The new kinds of music that were appearing and changing attitudes towards sex and the new kinds of writing in America – the Beat Poets – and in Russia. The general feeling that it was a new phase beginning was very liberating. It may have come largely from what was happening to me in my personal life, it's hard to sort out the chicken and the egg in these situations, but it was a period which I found very helpful, very enjoyable and there was happiness there. It was a very productive time and that, of course, makes you happy. For a writer, that's your whole job – to write. Anything else is secondary. So if you're writing, whatever else is happening in your life, that's good. The things that help you to write if you can identify them, you want to continue. If it's love or love of music or poetry or whatever it may be, if you can identify the sources of your happiness, you think long may these sources continue. The poems I wrote about John Scott were mostly positive poems about relationships which didn't have any happy outcome at all but the actual tension and frustration can lead to poetry as well. It seems to work both ways.

In the '60s I was probably encouraged to write a bit more openly. It was a gradual process and I don't think there was any time you could see a sudden change. I did write some love poems in the '60s that to anyone who was able to read between the lines were fairly open declarations. The one called 'Glasgow Green', which I wrote in 1963, was about homosexual activity in Glasgow Green late at night in the winter time. When I started writing that poem I felt it had to be written but I still couldn't do it really openly. The scene in the park is nightmarish and although you can't really work it out as other than homosexual, there's a sense of a mystery about it. I suppose that was the nearest I could get to being open in the early '60s, long before gay lib. It was published eventually and nothing terrible happened and now you get it taught in schools.

It wasn't till the '70s that I began thinking about the Middle East again. I think because it was so much in the news again. My memories were still very vivid and so I brought both the platonic man and the physical man into the poems 30 years after the events. These poems are in the sequence called *The New Divan*. The ones which are clear are the platonic ones, the one which is about the physical relationship is not so clear for it uses the word 'you' and that could be taken to be heterosexual.

We weren't politically active but John and I would talk about things when they were reported in the papers. We talked about the Gielgud case and Lord Montagu and Wildeblood and the distant possibility of a change in the law. The Gielgud thing I remember particularly because not long after Gielgud was charged one of his films was being shown at the Cosmo, what is now the Glasgow Film Theatre, and when his name appeared on the credits, there were hisses from the crowd and I thought – here's the intelligentsia's response to this poor man. I was never a great person for joining things and when the Scottish Homosexual Rights Group and so on were starting up I supported them but I never took an active part.

John and I went through all sorts of phases, great ups and downs, and I remember at the time when we weren't getting on too well and he wasn't seeing me that letters passed between him and my mother. Maybe she wrote first, maybe she saw I was unhappy in some way. She must have sensed it had something to do with this relationship and I think she may have written to him and said – why don't you two get together again? I didn't know about it until much later when he told me. I met his family and I think I was accepted. I never will know how much they knew about our relationship but they couldn't have avoided knowing it was a close relationship. When we went on holiday together they didn't raise any objection. They didn't talk about it, they just took it as one of those things. When he died I went to the funeral and his family gave me one of the cords to hold at the actual burial. I was surprised as it usually is only very close friends or family who are allowed to do this. They must have accepted then that I was to be given this position, which I was very glad to get. We'd had a bad quarrel a year before that and things weren't too good before his death. These are things you can't do anything about. I always regret it. The kind of quarrel that really comes out of nothing. Just blows up. Each person says things . . . really terrible things . . . you feel you'll never get back on an even keel again. Then the man dies and you can't say how sorry you were about it all. That was the one bad thing, bitter thing about that last year.

The poems I wrote about John Scott, all the love poems were very open to me but not, I suppose, to other people because the poems often don't give anything away. The lover is addressed as 'you' and not 'he' or 'she'. When it came to 1990, I was going to be 70 and I knew there would be lots of interviews coming up. I suppose it was fairly widely known that I was gay but, nevertheless, I had never properly declared the fact. I made up my mind I was going to be completely open and some of the poems of that time are perfectly straightforward in their declarations. That's a long time after the '60s when I maybe should have been doing it but I felt I couldn't do it then. I don't think anyone really enjoys living with a secret life going on underneath and I don't at all regret having done it. There were no bad results of having done it. Schools seem to be able to accept it and I haven't been taken off the Higher English syllabus. The gay theme comes out now and again in different ways but it's not the central theme of all my writing and so people who are teaching the work in schools or colleges can refer to it without bringing in my gayness at all. Most of my writing is not coming from a gay writer as such but from a writer who happens to be gay.

I am writing different kinds of things these days. I wrote some poems about a visit to America and some poems for an anthology of city poems. The anthology has one poem which is much more directly outspoken than some of the ones I have done in the past. I took a few months to do a translation of *Cyrano de Bergerac* for Communicado. I like the theatre and I thought it was time to give us a Scottish version of Cyrano. The real Cyrano, the 17th-century one, was gay and there is a very interesting gay subtext to the whole play. I could imagine a production of the play which could be very different from the normal way of doing it.

As a writer I try to remain open to experiences as they happen and I think, living in a city, you store them up in your mind and you hope that they can get into a poem some day. One poem, called 'Christmas Eve', would be an example of that – just sitting next to somebody on a bus and being propositioned in such a way that it was impossible to carry anything forward. Little instances of that kind I've often brought into poems and they're nearly always based on things that have happened and I enjoy the idea of bringing little dramatic incidents into poetry. The poem called 'Head' – a punning title – is about an incident that did, in fact, happen but in poetry it's often quite difficult to bring in things directly. Glasgow is very interesting for a writer. The absence of a strong literary tradition in Glasgow meant that for a long time it was hard to write about the reality of things but it's possible now. Incidents which you know to be deplorable you store in your mind and you may write about them in ways that you don't quite see at the moment. It's all grist to a writer's mill.

Christmas Eve

Loneliness of city Christmas Eves –
With real stars up there – clear – and stars
On poles and wires across the street, and streaming
Cars all dark with parcels, home
To families and the lighted window trees –

I sat down in the bus beside him – white jeans,
Black jerkin, slumped with head nodding
In sleep, face hidden by long black hair, hands
Tattooed on the four fingers ADEN 1967
And on the right hand five Christian crosses.
As the bus jerked, his hand fell on my knee,
Stayed there, lay heavily and alive
With blue carvings from another world
And seemed to hold me like a claw,
Unmoving. It moved. I rubbed my ear
To steal a glance at him, found him
Stealing a glance at me. It was not
The jerking of the bus, it was a proposition.
He shook his hair back, and I saw his face
For the first time, unshaven, hardman, a warning
Whether in Aden or Glasgow, but our eyes held
While that blue hand burned into my leg.

Half drunk, half sleeping – but half what, half what?
And his hand stirred again, my arm covered it
While the bus jolted round a corner.
'Don't ge' aff tae ah ge' aff.' – But the conductor
was watching, came and shook him, looked at me.
My ticket was up. I had to leave him sprawled there
With that hand that now seemed so defenceless
Lying on the seat I had left. Half down the stair
I looked back. The last thing I saw was Aden
And five blue crosses for five dead friends.

It was only fifteen minutes out of life
But I feel as if I was lifted by a whirlwind
And thrown down on some desert rocks to die
Of dangers as always far worse lost then run.

from

something leather

ALASDAIR GRAY

ALASDAIR GRAY

June is intelligent, and honest, and very lonely. She is also strikingly good looking, which does not help much. She likes admiration but most men's admiration becomes resentment when she refuses to let them bring it to a very ordinary sexual conclusion. She thinks slightly plainer women have an easier time. She was married once and that also ended for ordinary reasons. Her husband could not forgive her for earning more than he earned yet did not want her to stop work and have a child. At the time she was sorry. Now she is glad. Too many women, she thinks, use children to distract them from unsatisfying lives. Her salary from the civil service is now too big for her to risk losing the job, the job too unsatisfying to let her rest in it. She often dreams of taking a long break and finding work that pleases her, but perhaps (says her honesty) no such work exists. People who know what they want in life are guided to it by an obsession. June's only obsession is commonplace – she likes dressing well. When buying a garment which suits her rare kind of handsomeness she feels that life, after all, might become an exciting adventure. She has a large wardrobe of clothes to remind her of that wonderful, short-lived feeling. It does not stop her usually feeling like a Mercedes Benz forced to work as a taxi.

Her job has an advantage apart from the wage. By working overtime she can make Friday a holiday and walk about assessing fashions in shop windows and on the bodies of passers-by. Her favourite styles are those of the '30s and '40s which flirt elegantly or luxuriously with the human outline. On this clear summer afternoon nearly everything she sees annoys her, the prevailing styles shout aloud that times are tough. Young men with money wear floppy suits and stubble on their chins. Jackets, waistcoats, woollens, shirts and skirts are worn in eccentric layers as if put on fast in an emergency. The commonest fabric is denim; the commonest garment a shapeless jacket with huge pockets suggesting a labour camp. This has been popular for years and makers have given it a new lease of life by dyeing it to appear dirtied by rough usage. Jeans and skirts are also made from this denim. Some young people (June is no longer young) wear jeans they have deliberately ripped; why? The only elegant garment she glimpses is made of the toughest fabric of all. Someone slim and neat passes in a suit of gleaming black leather with silver zips. June has never worn leather but some shops sell nothing else. She experiences a faint, familiar thrill: she will hunt down an exciting new thing to wear. The leather shop welcomes her with a scent she finds comforting yet exotic – she has forgotten how good leather smells. But the skirts and jackets don't appeal to her and she does not even look at the trousers – trousers are not her style. An assistant asks what she is looking for.

'None of this, exactly,' says June glancing discontentedly along a rack, 'I want something more . . . something less . . .'

She is going to say 'conventional' but blushes instead. She does not exactly know what she wants.

'Perhaps you should have it made to order,' says the assistant briskly.

'Where?'

'The Hideout is quite near here – number 3798.'

June wanders meekly into the sunlight again but her meekness is on the surface. *Hideout* adds a spice of Wild West adventure to this hunt for something she cannot yet imagine.

The place is further than the assistant suggested. Beyond a crossroads June finds she has left the fashionable district. A poorer lot of people crowd along the cracked pavement but they look cheerful in sunlight. June is no snob, all that worries her is the absence of any place called The Hideout or numbered 3798. Between 2988 (a loan office) and 4040 (a betting shop) is a long row of boarded-up fronts. She walks up and down before these, excitement cooling to a familiar disappointment till she notices a car at the kerb: a cheap little Citroën with two wavy blue lines on the side. To the canvas roof, with great ingenuity, an arrow-shaped sign is fixed. A leather belt is stapled to the sign in a loop surrounding the words hideout leatherwear. The arrow points across the pavement at a dark little entry smelling of cat-piss and leading to steps worn to such a slant that June feels insecure on them. They bring her to a landing with a plank floor and three low doors, two faced with rusty metal and padlocked, one coloured vivid orange with a handwritten label saying press hard above a bell-button. June pressed it, hard.

She has gone through the shadowy entry and up these stairs with the uneasy excitement of a huntress following the game into a dangerous thicket, but when the door opens her uneasiness vanishes. A bright ordinary little woman in a print dress opens it and says, 'I'm sorry, come in. I can't attend to you right now because I'm finishing something for someone but if you can wait I'll be with you in a minute. What sort of thing are you looking for?'

She leads June down a short corridor to a long, low-ceilinged bar-looking room with six dusty windows above the shop fronts on the street. A sewing machine, a rack of hangers empty of garments, a table with tools and samples on it are almost the only furniture. In a corner of the carpetless plank floor is an electric kettle plugged to a wall socket, two mugs, a jar of coffee powder, a bag of sugar, and a radio playing pop music. Beside the sewing machine sits a woman who scowls at June as if she was intruding. She is very like the woman who opened the door, though plumper and with thick black hair cut straight across the brow and shoulders like the wig of a sphinx.

'I think,' says June hesitantly, 'I want a . . . skirt.'

'Sit down and look at some patterns,' says the woman pointing to a fat album on the table. 'I'll be with you in five minutes,' and she sits at the machine and resumes putting something through it while the other woman talks to her in a low penetrating voice which sounds conversational yet complaining.

The album has cuttings from catalogues and fashion magazines mounted on big pages under transparent film. As June turns these pages she grows more and more frustrated. They show all sorts of leather garments, some conventional, some bizarre, but nothing June would wear in the street. She is too old to enjoy dressing before a mirror. Why did she come here? She finds she is straining to hear phrases which penetrate the stuttering bursts of sewing-machine sound and the din of pop music.

'. . . had her eye on me but I had my eye on her . . .'

'. . . I said you don't buy what you don't like . . .'

'. . . hotpants isn't just her middle name it's her first and last . . .'

June shakes her head impatiently, turning the pages faster and faster until she reaches blank ones at the end. She is going to slam the book shut and leave when she sees the corner of a loose photograph protruding from those last pages. Pulling it out she discovers she is holding two black and white photographs, but for a long time the one on top has her whole attention.

A black leather skirt, calf-length and with a rear fastening of silver studs from waist to hem, is worn by a woman who is photographed from behind. It would be too tight if most of the studs were not unfastened but a few top ones are fastened to hide an arse made proud by her high-heeled shoes. The shoes and skirt are all she wears as she presses against the wall bars of a gymnasium, stretching one arm up to grasp a bar just beyond the reach of her fingertips. Then

June sees her wrist is handcuffed to that bar. Her free hand grips a bar at shoulder height, her legs are braced as far apart as possible to take all the weight she can off the steel bracelet round that wrist. Her head is flung backward. All that appears of it is a white line of brow and much unbound thick black hair cut straight across the shoulder in a way which reminds June of someone near her, but the reminder is not strong enough to break the dreamy enchantment cast by the photograph. If the woman gossiping by the sewing machine ('. . . and I said to her, I said, I said . . .') is the woman in the photograph she is more interesting, more encitingly beautiful in the photograph. Then June notices she is alone in that room, the voices are gossiping beside the front door, which slams. She hears someone approaching her and asking cheerily, 'Well? Have you found what you want?'

'Not . . . exactly,' says June after a pause, and as she still cannot draw her eyes from the photograph or bear to lay it down she starts talking as if the skirt, nothing but the skirt, is the thing she stares at, is all that interests her.

'A front fastening, I think, and . . .'

She hesitates, having no other ideas.

'Pockets?' asks the woman.

'Well . . . yes.'

'Big ones?'

'Perhaps . . .'

'Like hers?'

The woman takes the photograph uncovering the one beneath. It shows a tall lean woman in her early thirties, her scalp shaved quite bald, standing arrogantly astride. She wears big baggy suede overalls with the legs rolled above the knee. Saddlebag pockets on the thighs make them bulge out like jodhpurs but more noticeable is her smile of greedy pleasure, the thin cane she flexes in her hands.

'That's Miss Cain, our schoolteacher. Her real name is Harry – she's an artist. Lots of goodies in her pockets!' says the woman encouragingly. June stares, then nods, blushing.

'I know exactly what you want!' cries the woman enthusiastically.

She lays both photographs on the table, grabs a pad and sketches on it saying, 'Like this . . . and loops for the belt here . . . Why not a front *and* back fastening?'

June finds herself agreeing to a skirt she has no intention of wearing.

Then the woman slides the photos back into the album and says confidingly, 'I nearly died when I saw you with those.'

'Why?'

'They shouldn't be in that album – they're from an album my wicked clients use.'

'Wicked?' says June, pretending not to understand.

'Not *horribly* wicked. But they enjoy games not everyone enjoys, so they like to be careful. I don't blame them! I'm a bit wicked myself – that's why they trust me. Now I'm going to measure you.'

The woman kneels and as her light fingers put a tape round June's waist, hips, lower hip etcetera June looks absent-mindedly round the room. She sees no sign of another album.

'It's in a wee safe under the table,' says the woman, who is making notes in her pad. 'You see, these photos don't just show available dress designs, they show available . . . people, so they're rather tempting. Would you like a peep?'

She smiles at June who is too confused by having her mind read to say a word, but perhaps she nods because the woman shuts the pad briskly saying, 'I'll maybe allow you a peep when you come for the fitting. When will suit you?'

'Friday?'

'Sure! Anytime next Friday will do. Give me your phone number in case something happens and there's a delay. But there shouldn't be.'

June gives her phone number, asks the price of the skirt (which is reasonable) and offers a down payment.

'No need,' says the woman, smiling, 'I know you'll be back.'

'You seem even more remote from us than usual,' says June's boss to her in the office next Tuesday.

'I feel peculiar,' June admits.

'You looked flushed. Take a day off.'

'Maybe I will,' says June, but she knows what her disease is. She is haunted by daydreams of a picture book showing temptingly available victims and tyrants. Her heart beats faster at the memory. She feels – while knowing this irrational – close to a gladness and freedom she has not enjoyed since she was 11 and sex was a thrilling secret shared with a few special friends, not an anxious negotiation with a potentially dangerous adult. But that was long ago. To play truant from work and visit The Hideout before Friday and ask to see the wicked album will be admitting a sexual need. June has never in her life admitted a sexual need to another adult. She waits till Friday before returning to The Hideout, and forces herself to wait till mid-afternoon, instead of arriving like an eager little girl as soon as it opens.

And she stands on the cracked pavement between the loan office and the betting shop and stares at a space of reddish, brick-strewn gravel with a railway viaduct behind it. For a while she cannot believe the whole building has vanished. She fights the desolate frustration she feels by examining the rows of buildings on each side of the space, and going into a pub across the road from it, though it is the sort of pub where lonely women are stared at. She orders a gin and tonic and asks the barman, 'What happened to the tailoring business across the road?'

'Those shops were pulled down weeks ago.'

'Oh no – they were there last Friday.'

'Could be. But nobody's been in them for years.'

'But there was a . . . leathercraft shop upstairs in one. Called The Hideout. A small woman ran it. She advertised with a sign on a parked car.'

'She couldn't have. Parking's illegal on that side.'

June finishes her drink then goes to the fashionable leatherwear shop which gave her the address. The only information the assistant has is a card a stranger handed in, The Hideout name and address on it.

She says, 'These small firms come and go very quickly. Will I give you the address of another?'

June goes home to her room and kitchen flat, buying a bottle of sherry on the way.

She has a very hot bath, washes her hair, then sits in her dressing gown on the hearthrug, sipping sherry and listening to a record. This does not cheer her. She feels empty and old, with nothing much to expect from life. A second glass leaves her gloomier and fuddled. The telephone rings. She lifts the receiver.

'This is Donalda Ingles,' says an unfamiliar, anxious little voice. 'I've got your skirt.'

'*Who* are you?'

'Donalda. We met in The Hideout last week. Your skirt's ready!'

'I went there today and . . .'

'Yes, you saw what they did to us. Listen, can I bring it round?'

'Bring it here?'

'Yes. You aren't busy, are you? I mean, nobody's with you, are they?'

'No, but . . .'

'Give me your address and I'll bring it over right away, I'm sure you'll like it.'

There is an odd, pleading note in the little voice through the receiver. After a pause June gives her address and the voice says, 'I'll be there in 20 minutes.'

June goes thoughtfully to her wardrobe. She is about to choose a dress when she changes her mind and puts on pants, bra and white cotton blouse with the dressing gown on top. She will wear the skirt for the maker of it, if for nobody else. This decision makes her feel young again.

The entryphone rings. June presses the admission switch and goes to the door. A woman in a long waterproof coat and carrying a suitcase comes up the stairs to June's landing and stands before her saying, 'Hello! Don't you remember me?'

It is the small plump woman with black hair like the sphinx's wig.

'Yes, but I didn't expect you, I expected –'

'Oh, Senga couldn't come, she's very busy from having to shift, you see, and she thought you'd rather see me anyway.'

'Why?' says June, letting the woman in and closing the door.

'Senga gets these notions. I never argue with her. This is a very nice room, do you mind if I take off my coat?'

She asks this as if expecting to be refused. In The Hideout she seemed sullen and plaintive. Now she is an intriguing mixture of boldness and shyness, as if shoving herself forward against her will. When June says, 'Of course, take it off!' she hesitates before quickly unbuttoning and dropping it on the sofa beside the suitcase, then she stands gazing at June in a helpless, pleading way. With a white silk blouse she is wearing exactly the high-heeled shoes and leather skirt she wore in the photograph, and to prove it she lifts both hands to shoulder height and turns round till she faces June again, having shown the rear fastening more than half undone. And June knows she is being seduced and has partly wanted it. Her heart beats hard and fast, yet she is able to smile with perfect confidence at the plump, sexy-looking, nervous little woman. Though June has never been seduced by a woman before, the situation is a familiar one.

'What about my skirt?' she asks. Donalda nods, opens the case, takes the skirt out. June slips off her dressing gown and stands with folded arms before the wardrobe mirror. Donalda kneels and fastens it round her, buckling the belt, patting and smoothing the leather over waist, stomach, arse and tops of the thighs and all the time murmuring, 'There, isn't that nice? Aren't you lovely?'

June looks down on her with some of the loneliness, some of the contemptuous superiority she always feels with people who greatly desire her, though looking at the mirror she notices wryly that her own skirt is far more challengingly whorish than the one Donalda wears.

She also sees, as well as feeling, Donalda's arms embrace her waist, Donalda's face press into the angle of her neck and shoulder, Donalda's lips brush her ear and whisper, 'There's a present for you in the right pocket.'

June slides her hand under the pocket flap and pulls out the photographs which enchanted her in The Hideout. She stares at them as Donalda leads her to the soft rug before the fire, stares at them as she responds to the little beseeching murmurs and hand pats by which Donalda brings her to lie down and open to her. She even stares at them while absentmindedly, with her free hand, returning some of Donalda's caresses. Donalda sobs, 'Oh, you devil! You lovely devil! You don't care for me at all, do you? It's her you wanted Senga to send!'

'I'm not sure,' murmurs June, looking from the photo of the tempting victim to that of the exciting tyrant. Which does she like best? Which would she like to be? She really does not know.

Much later June lies with closed eyes, half satisfied and half dissatisfied as she always feels after lovemaking. She is conscious of Donalda's body against her back, Donalda's hand resting on her thigh, Donalda's small voice explaining or complaining about something. 'You haven't once asked who I am or how I feel or what I want in life – I think you care for nobody but yourself but I must tell you about me. I came from a really big family, three older brothers and three younger sisters and I had to help my Mum look after the lot of them. I really loved my Mum, she was a really good woman who never thought of herself, she made herself old before her time slaving from morning till night for all those men and young lassies who never gave a damn for her. Well, when I turned 15 I couldn't take any more – I was sick of helping her so I left home, I suppose because I'm wicked. We all have wicked dreams, don't we? And unless we bring one of our wicked dreams just a wee bit to life we live like zombies – the living dead – slaves like my Mammy, right? Answer me! *Please!*'

'Right,' says June, who feels too tired to disagree or think much and has begun to find Donalda Ingles a bore.

'I want to ask you another thing. Have you any arrangements this weekend? Are you going to see someone or are they coming here to see you?'

'I've made no arrangements,' says June, and to stop Donalda suggesting one adds, 'I like weekends to myself.'

'Anyway,' says Donalda, after a pause, 'when I left my Mammy I got into big trouble. I won't go into details, they would only sicken you – I had a baby and all that. It was Senga who saved me. She's not much older than me, we were pals at school, but she's as sure of what to do as my Mammy is, though my Mammy is a slave and Senga is definitely a boss. When I help Senga I'm helping myself because . . . don't laugh . . . Senga is a fairy godmother who makes dreams come true. She's so good at it she earns her living that way. She told me to do this with you, please let me, it won't hurt,' says Donalda. 'Just turn over a bit.'

June obediently turns over. She hears nothing now but the unfastened skirt and the belt, which has several straps and buckles. June lets Donalda draw her wrists behind her back, cross them above the belt and loop a strap round them. The pressure of the strap suddenly becomes almost painful and June finds her wrists fastened there.

'And now?' she placidly asks. Donalda stands, goes to the kitchen and returns with three clean glasses. These she lays on the table and fills from the sherry bottle.

'What's happening?' asks June, puzzled. Donalda dips into the suitcase and brings out a radio telephone and a wide strip of adhesive bandage. She says, 'A couple in a car downstairs have been waiting to see you so I'm asking them up. If you start screaming I'll gag you with this bandage.'

June is too astonished to scream. She tries to stand which is hard without hands and impossible when Donalda sits on her legs and puts an arm round her neck.

'Listen!' says Donalda, and her voice is not hard or cruel. 'Please believe this, Senga and I make other people's dreams come true but we haven't begun to help you yet – you're so locked up in yourself you don't know what your dreams are. You're under a spell and we won't let you go till we've broken that spell. Because you're the loveliest thing we've ever met. But first, before Senga brings the teacher here . . .'

She fastens her mouth on June's mouth in a kiss which is almost a bite, and for a moment June enjoys a melting delicious weakness like nothing she has known.

We will return to her later.

from

stronger than death

MANDA SCOTT

The water was cold, breathlessly cold. It burned, hotter than the sun, making wax of muscles that should have been swimming so that I felt like a rag doll, weighed down by the water. I swam in small circles in the weed-strung water near the edge and then turned back and stepped out onto the grass and the dry warmth of the towel. Dee is immune to the cold. She reached the rock of the far shore, turned and pushed off and swam back towards me in a strong, rhythmic crawl; stroke after stroke making white waves in the green ice of the water. The pale blonde of her hair, sleeked down on her scalp like a swimming cap, grew darker with every stroke. By the time she reached the far bank beside me for the second time, it was black. I thought she might come out then but she flipped on her back and reached out again and swam, more lazily now, to the place at the head of the loch where the river drops down from the higher rock of the ben. She found a rock with a flat top and pulled herself up onto it and dived off again, neat and clean, and raced, a full, thrashing butterfly, back to the shore. Her breath was coming hard when she stopped, the way it does when she runs. She stood up in the shallows, the water streaming down from her shoulders, wet hair hanging straight like the weed, eyes and teeth bright against darker, sun-drunk skin and

I'd say that her smile, this once, was real. She swivelled round, on one heel, to face me.

'That was good. Thank you. I'm glad I came.'

'Good.' I threw her a towel and she came to sit on the grass beside me, rubbing away the jitters and the goose bumps and the wrinkling skin. 'There are apples in the saddle pack.'

'You're just desperate to get me to eat something, aren't you?'

'No. I'm just desperate to eat. You don't have to join in.'

An apple lobbed onto the turf by my cheek. 'Has the headache gone yet?'

'Totally. Yours?'

'I didn't have a headache.'

'But it has gone?'

No answer; just a hard, crunching bite; white teeth into crisp, acid skin. Then: 'Roll over, my towel's wet.'

I rolled over, one arm angled up to shade my eyes from the sun. Dee lay down on her stomach beside me, elbows propped on the grass, working her way through the apple. I felt the cool of the water and the warm of her skin beneath it, the soft shift of her breathing. We lay in silence for a while and then, in time, I heard her voice, quiet, musing, 'There was someone else, wasn't there, before Nina?'

I wasn't expecting that, not at all. I haven't thought that far back for a long, long time. I'm not sure I want to, particularly. I closed my eyes to the sun. 'Her name was Bridget.'

'Were you together long?'

'Eight years. And then another four when we should have been but I was too pig-headed to go home and apologise for being a total shit.'

'And then she found someone else?'

'No. Then she died.'

'Oh.' A soft sound in the silence. 'I'm sorry.'

'Thanks.'

The apple cores lay on the grass by my hand. I picked them up and took them to the horses; tossed one over to Balder out at the place where the grass meets the heather. Maddie came in for hers, blowing warm breath on my shoulder, so much more gentle than the colt. I ran my hand across the brown and white patches of her skin as she ate. I always wanted a skewbald. It took years to persuade Sandy that she wasn't going to taint his precious breeding plans and even now he isn't sure. Colour prejudice is alive and well and living in central Scotland. I hadn't thought, until now, of what Bridget might have said to that.

The mare finished her share and pushed her nose to my chest, turning me back where I came from. Dee lay quiet on the towel, her hands clasped, chin looped on the hammock of her fingers, staring out across the loch. The breeze was up, cutting small ruffles on the surface and lifting the fine, white-in-gold weed of her hair. The dog closed her eyes and stretched out in the shade of the saddles. Nothing else moved. I walked over and sat, cross-legged, on the towel.

'Does it not feel like a betrayal?' she asked. Her eyes were still on the loch. Her voice was soft and rounded and smooth, like a rock from the river. Questing but not intruding.

'Does what not feel like a betrayal?'

'Being with Nina.'

Difficult. I had to think about that one, too. Then eventually: 'No.'

'Why not?'

'It's different. I'm different. She's different.'

'Even at the start?'

The start was hard for all kinds of reasons. Bridget, oddly, wasn't one of them. 'No. Never. Mostly, I wanted to be able to tell her what was happening.'

A curlew flew over, silent. I was glad. I didn't need, just then, that kind of keening.

'Do you think she knows?'

'About Nina? I don't know.'

'But it would be good to think so?'

'Maybe.' But if she doesn't, it's because it doesn't matter.

Another space. Her face was quite still. I am learning, I think, to see beneath that. I picked a stalk of grass and chewed on the end. It's

15 years since she went into medicine. It's a long, long time to be single. 'Dee, has there been anyone for you since Beth?'

'No.'

'Because it would feel like a betrayal?'

'I think so.' She rolled over, onto her side, facing me. She reached out a hand. It slid into mine, hand in glove. 'And I haven't wanted it. Yet.'

Her eyes are grey-green and quite still, with tiny pinpoint pupils narrowed down by the sun. Her hand is cool and still damp from the water. Beads of water gather along her collarbone. A moment ago, they rocked with the rhythm of her breathing. Now, they are still.

In another time and another place, this could be so different.

'Dee . . .'

Her hand changed. It didn't move, but it changed. Her eyes stayed on mine. 'You're not single. I know.' She smiled. A real smile. No masks. 'It's okay. You can relax . . . Life is complicated enough. I wasn't going to do anything. Just that . . . we needed to know. *I* needed to know.'

'Thank you.'

'You're too good a friend.'

'Thank you.'

She moved away half an inch. Her hand stayed in mine. I squeezed it. 'Thank you.'

She squeezed back. The smile teased, gently and without rancour. 'Say something different.'

'I can't. There's nothing left. You said it all.'

'No.' She pulled herself up and sat facing me, knee to knee. 'Not all of it. There's "life's too short" as well.'

'Maybe. That one doesn't fit so well with all the others.'

'I know. That's why I didn't say it. And then again . . .' she swivelled her hand and we sat, palm to palm, fingers splayed, '. . . there's more to life than sex.'

'There is.'

I reached out my free hand, ran my fingers through the straggled damp of her hair. 'You need to ask Lee about that.' I changed the palm press, slid my hand back into hers. 'I'm sorry. Do you mind?'

'Of course.' Her fingers looped through mine and locked. Her smile was distant, gently mocking. 'But I'd mind more if you said anything else.' She stood up, pulling the towel with her as she went. 'You're one of the few constant things in my life, Kellen Stewart. I couldn't handle it just now if you changed.' She reached down a hand, lifted me up to my feet. 'It's getting late. If we don't go soon, they'll send out search parties. Shall we go down and see if we can find something in the freezer to surprise them for dinner?'

The fire glows low in the grate. The windows hang open, the doors with them. The up draught of the flames draws air into the room more than if the fire was not lit. If I need an excuse for a fire, that is it; and the cat likes it, there is that as well.

A bottle of wine stands on the hearth, close to empty; the dregs in the bottom are too warm now to be worth finishing. Dee is in bed in the spare room, chaste in a borrowed T-shirt with the promise of spare clothes for the morning. She's Nina's size more than mine. Not quite so angular, perhaps, but not far off. We'll find something.

I lie back on the rug in front of the fire. The cat stretches out beside me, purring his ancient-cat purr. He was Bridget's before he was ever mine, the last of the links to a past that feels so long ago, it could be another life. Except there are memories and things learned, which make a difference to the way we live now. It is not good to make the same mistakes too often.

'Drink?'

'If there's something cold.'

'There's apple juice in the fridge.' Bare feet scuff across the floor. A glass arrives on the hearth. Firelight makes it amber, turns the juice to liquid gold. The sharp, bright taste of it clears the mellow memory of the wine. Nina sits on the floor, legs crossed at the ankles, leaning back against the weight of the fireside chair. I roll over and look up into wide, deep walnut eyes. Eyes with a question. She reaches out to touch the cat. He is our point of common contact. 'Do we have something to discuss?'

I sit up with my back to the other chair. That she feels free to ask says something. I stand my glass, with care, on the hearth and shake my head. 'No.'

'Not yet? Or at all?'

'Not at all. Not now, not ever.'

'Why not?'

I have to think about that one. It is important for both of us to know, for now and for later. There are words, and there is the truth. Only one of these matters. The last of the flames flickers down, leaving a bank of peat flowing like lava in the grate. Her eyes hold mine, mellow in the reddening light, still searching. In time I find the answer. I stretch out a foot, push it up against hers. We don't need the cat as intermediary. 'She isn't you.'

A hand reaches down. Cool fingers wrap around my ankle. She smiles, a half-lit quirk of a smile.

'Thank you.'

It was Wednesday night. For a space, the world was at peace.

from

trumpet

JACKIE KAY
JACKIE KAY

I never fancied boys; no, I've always been 100 per cent heterosexual, except for those times when I was about 16 and my mates and me would have a joint and a communal wank listening to Todd or Genesis or Pink Fucking Floyd. Or watching *The Old Grey Whistle Test* on the box. I don't like that hippy music any more, man. It was just a phase.

Why do people want to make other people proud? What's that about? It's neurotic, isn't it? Kids get fed that crap before they walk. Even walking for your parents is something to be proud of, your first wobbly steps. It's a load of balls, that's what it is. I spent too much time saying, Look at me, Daddy, so much that I never fucking looked at him.

We didn't talk much about me being adopted. I wasn't that interested in my real parents. I mean my thinking was if they weren't interested in me, then I wasn't interested in them. Simple as that. My mother would tell me that this other woman would have loved me and found it hard to give me up, I just said yeah, yeah and privately thought, Bollocks. I mean if you love a kid you keep them, if you don't you give them up. Simple. Money don't matter, what people think don't matter. If you want a kid and you get a bun in your oven, you'll fucking cherish the whining squirming brat, or not. If I'd got the chance I'd have probably liked to see a photograph of my mother and one of my father. I don't even know which one was black or where the black one came from. Haven't got a clue. People are always coming up to me and asking if I'm from Haiti, Morocco, Trinidad, Tobago, Ghana, Nigeria, Sierra Leone, Jamaica. Some asshole the other week was convinced I came from Haiti. You look identical to the people there, he said. Stopped me dead in the street and says, Hey, are you from Haiti? I dunno, I says. Then I thought the next fucker that asks me where I come from, I'm going to say yes I come from Haiti, Morocco, Trinidad or any place they ask. What does it matter anyway? My father always told me he and I were related the way it mattered. He felt that way too about the guys in his bands, that they were all part of some big family. Some of them were white, some black. He said they didn't belong anywhere but to each other. He said you make up your own bloodline, Colman. Make it up and trace it back. Design your own family tree, what's the matter with you? Haven't you got an imagination? Tell me really, that's what I kept saying, tell me where your father was really from. Look, Colman, he said, Look, Colman, I could tell you a story about my father. I could say he came off a boat on a cold winter day, a boat that stopped at the port of Glasgow. The port of Glasgow when Glasgow was a place where all the ships wanted to go. He came off that ship and although it was cold and grey, he liked it. He liked Glasgow, so he settled. Or I could say my father was a black American who left America because of segregation and managed to find his way to Scotland where he met my mother. Or I could say my father was a soldier or a sailor who was sent here by his army or his navy. Or I could say my father was from an island in the Caribbean whose name I don't know because my mother couldn't remember it. Or never bothered to ask. And any of these stories might be true, Colman. It drove me mad. Which one, I said. Which one is true? Doesn't matter a dam, he said. You pick. You pick the one you like best and that one is true. It doesn't change me who my father was or where he came from and it certainly doesn't change you, he said.

He was wrong about that. He was wrong. The stupid bastard was wrong. I'm sure he used to be right. I'm sure when I was a little kid he was right about everything. He was so right his face shone. His hair looked clever. He was so right then and I went about the place trying to remember all the things he told me and the way he told them. I'd copy some of his big words. Kidology, that was one. Or colossal, that was another. Or impertinent, facetious, irreversible.

My father didn't like discussing his family. He had no old photographs of himself when he was a kid, not one. I suppose if I look in their house I could find some photographs of Josephine Moore hiding somewhere. Unless he cut himself up or burnt himself to hide the evidence. I hope he didn't. I hope I can find some. If I saw a photograph of her, I could convince myself that I'm not living some weird Freudian dream, some fucked-up dream where I don't know my father, my mother or myself. I don't know any of us anymore. He has made us all unreal. It doesn't matter where your father comes from, Colman, he said. Like fuck it doesn't. For all I know there could be some custom in one of those Caribbean islands, some annual carnival where everyone changes sex, dresses up as their opposite. Some big island carnival where all the transvestite islanders play steel bands and float on floats, heavily masked and made up so that no one can recognise anyone. I can't believe the stuff I'm thinking now. It's crap. Pure crap. I know it's crap, but that doesn't stop me from thinking it, from it floating into my head – all the scum and shit, drifting and sliding through my filthy mind.

He was wrong. He was wrong about everything.

I'm not bothered about knowing about those blood parents of mine. My mother told me a few bits about what they did. All they do is cause pain – parents, blood parents or Mickey Mouse parents, all they do is mess with your head. Not to be trusted, man. Shit, I wouldn't have kids. No way.

All I did was get born. I came into this world weighing a modest 6lbs and 2ozs according to my mother. I've always remembered those numbers; I was a lightweight. But my mother told me there was a big fucking hurricane around the time I was born. Blew the trees in our street down and several slates off the roof. Made quite a commotion. The winds were stark mad when I arrived at the Elsie Inglis hospital in Edinburgh. I'm still a skinny fucker. No meat on me. Tall as fuck and skinny. When I went to India I looked like a walking dead man. Got the runs and lost a stone and a half. My father said to me when I got back, you need to put on some weight, Cole. He called me Cole when he was being nice. My mother always called me Colman. I didn't ask to be born. I didn't ask to be adopted. Why should I be grateful to anybody? I was born under a sleeping star. An inebriated star. Somebody wasn't paying no attention. First this, then that. That's the story of my life. Nobody was watching out for me. They were too busy watching out for each other.

That's about all I can figure out. Some people get all the luck. There were guys like that at my school. They'd get chosen for the sports teams, they'd get the best-looking girls, they never wore glasses, especially not those extra thick ones, or trouser patches, or naff shoes. They just looked cool. I wore glasses. Don't anymore as you can see. I'm vain as fuck now. Whoever invented contact lenses ought to be knighted. I got a double-barrel name: Darky-Specky. I always thought it funny when teachers tried to explain racism to kids by saying, You wouldn't like to be called Freckles or Specky now, would you? But all that means nothing to this. Nothing.

My father had tits. My father didn't have a dick. My father had tits. My father had a pussy. My father didn't have any balls. How many people had fathers like mine?? Which chat line could I ring up for this one? Imagine it flashing up on the screen after a programme about father/mothers, trani parents or whatever the fuck you'd call them: if any of this relates to you and you need someone to talk to, please ring blah blah blah. The line will be open for the next 24 hours. Some things those fuckers haven't dreamt of, I'm telling you. I could ring round the whole country and never find anybody that's gone through what I'm going through, I bet you.

I'm going to track him down. I'm going to track my father's life down, back to when he was a girl in Morton, under the unassuming name Josephine Moore. Josey. Jose, Joss.

But where did he get the Moody? Or was that just moody blues? I'll write his fucking biography. I'll tell his whole story. I'll be his Judas. That's what Oscar Wilde said, isn't it? My dad often quoted it and laughed. 'Every man needs his disciples but it's Judas that writes the biography.' I used to be my father's disciple. Not any fucking more, mate. I've gone over to the other side.

I went into that funeral parlour and the man, the funeral man, takes me aside. He's got a look on his face I know I won't forget. Half awkward, half pure glee. Like things are suddenly looking up for him. He calls me Mr Moody. I think maybe he doesn't get all that many famous dead bodies and he's dead chuffed. Mr Moody, he says, I'm not quite sure how to put this, but it had better be me who tells you rather than the media, I am assuming of course that you don't know already. He waits. I see him reading my face. Know what already, I say, thinking the guy's a pillock. When I undressed your father to perform my routine duties, I discovered . . . I'm waiting for him. I think he's going to say he discovered my father had died of some other illness or that he discovered some weird mark on his body or that he discovered my father had committed suicide. I'm waiting. He's drawing it out. What the fuck has he discovered, that my father is still alive?

When I undressed your father, Mr Moody, I discovered that she is a woman. I had to have him repeat that sentence. The sentence sounded wrong to me. She is a woman. I thought the guy must be getting paid to perform some sick joke on me. Perhaps they have organisations where instead of sending a live kissogram to a birthday party, you send a weird deathogram to a funeral parlour. The man must not be the real man. I tell him I want to see the real undertaker, the mortician, whatever the fuck you call it, your boss. I said, is this your idea of a joke, you sick bastard? Who has put you up to this? I'm shaking him. Pulling his stupid thin lapels back and forth. This is all quite understandable, he says. Don't fuck with me, I says. He takes me through to where the body is. Through to the cold parlour and shows me my father. I see him naked and it is only now that I realise that this is the first time in my life that I have seen my father naked. The funeral man shows me some surgical bandages that he says were wrapped rightly around my father's chest to cover his 'top'. I take a quick look. But that look is still in my head now. It has stayed in my head – the image of my father in a woman's body. Like some pervert. Some psycho. I imagine him now smearing lipstick on a mirror before he died.

I walked out of that place as fast as I could. I said thank you for letting me know to the funeral man. The sky was bright blue that day and it was sunny. Hot. I was sweating. Everyone was complaining about the weather. I remember wondering if I'd ever be able to talk about anything so ordinary again. What a fucking luxury it seemed to stand around and say, Isn't it hot? A woman in a white top said to an old woman who was dressed for winter, 'Isn't this insufferable. Freak hot weather. Freak's the word.' I ran along repeating that to myself, 'Freak's the word.' I stopped and hung down to my toes and took a deep breath. My heart racing. Then I started up again. I was soaked. My hair was stuck to my head. My trousers were wet. The streets were on fire. Maybe I could just melt, I remember thinking, just melt away.

pictures

JAMES KELMAN

He wasn't really watching the picture he was just sitting there wondering on things; the world seemed so pathetic the way out was a straight destruction of it, but that was fucking daft, thinking like that; a better way out was the destruction of himself, the destruction of himself meant the destruction of the world anyway because with him not there his world wouldn't be either. That was better. He actually smiled at the thought; then glanced sideways to see if it had been noticed. But it didn't seem to have been. There was a female sitting along the row who was greeting. That was funny. He felt like asking her if there was a reason for it. A lot of females gret without reason. The maw was one. So was the sister, she gret all the time. She was the worst. Whenever you caught her unawares that was what would be happening, she would be roaring her eyes out. The idea of somebody roaring their eyes out, their eyes popping out their sockets because of the rush of water. Or maybe the water making them slippery inside the sockets so they slipped out, maybe that was what it was, if it was anything even remotely literal. No doubt it would just prove to be a total figure of speech: eyes did not go popping out of sockets. There was a sex scene playing. The two actors playing a sex scene, the female one raising the blanket to go down as if maybe for

125

oral intercourse, as if maybe she was going to suck him. Maybe this is why the woman was greeting along the row; maybe she once had this bad experience where she was forced into doing that very selfsame thing, years ago, when she was at a tender age, or else just it was totally against her wishes maybe. And she would not want reminding of it. And look what happens, in she comes to see a picture in good faith and innocence, and straightaway has to meet up with that terrible ancient horror.

Or else she enjoyed her feelings of anguish and had come along because of it, a kind of masochism or something, having heard from one of her pals about the sort of explicit – and maybe even exploitative – sex scenes to expect if she did. That was the director to blame anyway. In the pictures he was involved in something like this usually happened, and there was usually violence as well, like in this one murder. And people would end up in bad emotional states. Was it right that it should be like this? It was okay for somebody like him – the director – but what about other folk, ordinary folk, them without security, the overall security, the ones that actually went to watch his fucking pictures! The thought was enough to make you angry but it was best to just find it funny if you could, if you could manage it. He nodded and started grinning – it was best to. But it wasn't funny at all in fact it was quite annoying, really fucking annoying, and you could get angry about it, the way these bastards in the film industry got away with it.

And there was that female now, her along the row. He felt like shouting at her: What's up missus? Something wrong?

God Almighty but, the poor woman, maybe there *was* something bad up with her; he felt like finding out, maybe he should ask, maybe it was some bastard in a chair nearby, maybe wanking or something because of the sex scene, and here was the woman within perception distance – listening distance – having to put up with it, and it maybe reminding her of a terrible time when she was younger, just a lassie, and was maybe forced into some sort of situation, some kind of similar kind of thing. So fucking awful the way lassies sometimes get treated.

But it had to come back to the director, he it was to blame, it was this movie making the guy wank in the first place, if he hadn't been showing the provocative sexy scenes it wouldn't be fucking happening. There was a lot to be said for censorship. If a censor had seen this he would have censored it and then the woman maybe wouldn't be greeting. But no, it was more serious than that. Definitely. It was. She was definitely greeting for a reason, a real reason, she had to be – it was obvious; it had just been going on too long. If it had stopped once the scene changed then it would have been different, but it didn't. And the woman actor was back up the bed and her and the guy were kissing in the ordinary mouth-to-mouth clinch so if the oral carry-on had been the problem it was all over now and the woman should have been drying her tears. So it was obviously serious and had nothing to do with sex at all – the kind that was up on the screen at least. Maybe he should ask her, try to help. There were no attendants about. That was typical of course for matinee programmes, the management aye worked short-handed, cutting down on overheads and all the rest of it. This meant attendants were a rarity and the audience ran the risk of getting bothered by idiots. Once upon a time a lassie he knew was a cinema attendant. She used to have to walk down the aisle selling ice-creams, lollipops and popcorn at the interval; and they tried to get her to wear a short mini-skirt and do wee curtseys to the customers. But they obviously didn't know this lassie who was a fucking warrior, a warrior. She quite liked wearing short mini-skirts but only to suit herself. She used to get annoyed with the management for other reasons as well; they used to get her to wear this wee badge with her name on it so it meant all the guys looked at it and knew what it was and they shouted it out when they met her on the street. Heh, Susan! Sussaaaaan! And then they would all laugh and make jokes about her tits. It was really bad. And bad as well if you were out with her if you were a guy because it meant you wound up having to get involved and that could mean a doing if you were just one against a few. She was good too, until she fucked off without telling him. He phoned her up one night at tea-time and she wasn't in, it was her flatmate. And her flatmate told him she had went away, she had just went away. She had been talking about it for a while but it was still unexpected when it happened. Probably Manchester it was she went to. He had had his chance. He could have went with her. She hadn't asked him, but he could have if he had wanted. It was his own fault he hadn't, his own fault. She had given him plenty of opportunities. So it was his own fault. So he never heard of her again. It was funny the way you lost track of folk, folk you thought you would know for life; suddenly they just weren't there and you were on your ownsome. This seemed to happen to him a lot. You met folk and got on well with them but then over a period of time yous drifted away from each other – the same as the guys you knew at school, suddenly yous never even spoke to each other. That was just that, finished, fucking zero. It was funny. Sometimes it was enough to make you greet. Maybe this is what was up with the female along the row, she was just lonely, needing somebody to talk to God he knew the feeling, that was him as well – maybe he should just actually lean across and talk to her. Could he do that? So incredible an idea. But it was known as communication, you started talking to somebody, your neighbour. Communication. You took a deep breath and the rest of it, you fucking just leaned across and went 'Hullo there!' Except when it's a male saying it to a female it becomes different. She had the hanky up at the side of her eyes. She looked fucking awful. He leaned over a bit and spoke to her:

Hullo there missis. Are you okay?

The woman glanced at him.

He smiled. He shrugged and whispered, You were greeting and eh . . . you alright?

She nodded.

I couldn't get you something maybe, a coffee or a tea or something, they've got them at the foyer . . .

She stared at him and he got a sudden terrible dread she was going to start screaming it was fucking excruciating it was excruciating you felt like stuffing your fingers into your ears, he took a deep breath.

There wasn't anybody roundabout except an old dear at the far end of the row. That was lucky.

Maybe there *was* something up with her right enough. Or else maybe she was fucking mental – mentally disturbed – and just didn't have anywhere to go. Genuine. Poor woman. God. But folk were getting chucked out on the street these days; healthy or unhealthy, it didn't matter, the powers-that-be just turfed you out and they didn't care where you landed, the streets were full of cunts needing looked after, folk that should have been in nursing homes getting cared for. She was maybe one of them, just in here out the cold for a couple of hours peace and quiet. And then look at what she has to contend with up on the bloody screen . . .! God sake! In for a couple of hours peace and quiet and you wind up confronting all sorts of terrible stuff in pictures like this one the now. Maybe censors were the answer. Maybe they would safeguard folk like this woman. But how? How would they do it, the censors, how would they manage it? No by sticking the cinemas full of Walt Disney fucking fairyland. Who would go for a start? No him nayway, he hated that kind of shite. Imagine paying the entrance fee for that, fucking cartoons. He leant across:

Ye sure you don't want a coffee?

She shut her eyes, shaking her head for a moment. She wasn't as old as he had thought either. She laid the hand holding the hanky on her lap and the other hand she kept at the side of her chin, her head now tilted at an angle. She kept looking at the screen.

I was going to get one for myself. So I could get one for you while I was at it . . .

She turned to face him then; and she said, Could you?

Aye, that's what I'm saying.

Thanks, you're a pal.

Milk and sugar?

Just milk.

He hesitated but managed to just get up, giving her a swift smile and not saying anything more, just edging his way along the row. He had to pass by the old dear sitting in the end seat and she gave him a look before holding her shopping bags in to her feet to let him past, and he nodded to her quite briskly. He walked up the aisle and down the steps, pushing his way out into the corridor. Thick carpets and dim lighting. He grinned suddenly, then began chuckling. How come he had nodded at the old dear like that? She was as old as his grannie! God Almighty! But it was to show her he was relaxed. That was how he had done it, that was how he had done it. If he hadn't been relaxed he would never have bloody managed it because it would have been beyond him.

Cinema 2 was showing a comedy. He had seen it a week ago. He wasn't that keen on comedies, they were usually boring. He continued past the corridor entrance. There was an empty ice-cream carton sitting on the floor in such a way you felt somebody had placed it there intentionally. Probably they had. He used to have the selfsame habit when he was a boy – 13 or something – he used to do things to make them seem like accidental events. If he was smoking and finished with the fag he would stick it upright on the floor to make it look like somebody had just tossed it away and it had landed like that as a fluke.

He used to go about doing all sorts of stupid things. Yet when you looked at them; they weren't all that fucking stupid.

What else did he used to do? He used to leave stuff like empty bottles standing on the tops of stones and boulders, but trying to make it look like they had just landed that way accidentally. To make folk imagine alien things were happening here on planet Earth and they were happening for a reason, a purpose.

He was a funny wee cunt when he was a boy. Looking back you had to admit it.

The woman at the kiosk passed him the change from the till; she was in the middle of chatting with the cashier and didn't watch him after she had put the money on the counter so he lifted a bar of chocolate, slid it up his jacket sleeve. One was plenty. He took the two wee containers of milk and the packet of lump sugar for himself.

It was raining outside. He could see folk walking past with the brollies up. And the streetlights were on. It would soon be tea-time.

He didn't take the chocolate bar from his sleeve until along the corridor and beyond the Cinemas 1 and 2, which were the most popular and had the biggest auditoriums – but there were usually cunts talking in them, that was the drawback, when you were trying to listen to the movie, they held fucking conversations. He had to lay the cartons of coffee down on the floor, then he stuck his hand in his side jacket pocket, letting the bar slide straight in from the sleeve. He was going to give it to her, the woman. He wasn't that bothered about chocolate himself. And anyway, in his experience females liked chocolate more than males. They had a sweet tooth.

That was one of these incredible expressions, a sweet tooth. What did it actually mean? He used to think it meant something like a soft tooth, that you had a tooth that was literally soft, made of something like soft putty. When he was a boy he had a sweet tooth. But probably all boys had sweet tooths. And all lassies as well. All weans the world over in fact, they all liked sweeties and chocolate, ice-cream and lollipops, popcorn.

She was sitting in a semi-motionless way when he got back to the seat and it was like she was asleep, her eyelids not flickering at all. Here's your coffee, he said, milk with no sugar, is that right.

Ta.

He sat down in his old seat after an eternity of decision-making to do with whether or not he could just sit down next to her, on the seat next to hers; but he couldn't, it would have been a bit out of order, as if just because he had bought her a fucking coffee it gave him the right of fucking trying to sit next to her and chat her up, as if he was trying to get off with her – which is what women were ay having to put up with. The best people to be women were men because of the way they were, the differences between them, their sexuality, because they could get sex any time they like just about whereas men were usually wanting it all the time but couldn't fucking get it – it was a joke, the way it worked like that, a joke of nature, them that wanted it no getting it and them that didn't want it having to get it all the time. The bar of chocolate. He took it out his pocket and glanced at it; an Aero peppermint; he passed it across, having to tap her elbow because she was staring up at the screen.

Here. It's a spare one. He shrugged, I'm no needing it. I'm no really a chocolate-lover anyway, to be honest, I've no got a sweet tooth, the proverbial sweet tooth. He shrugged again as he held it out to her.

Oh I don't want that, she said out loud, her nose wrinkling as she frowned, holding her hand up to stop him. And he glanced sideways to see if folk had heard her and were maybe watching. He whispered:

How no? It's alright.

Oh naw pal I just don't eat them – Aero peppermints – any kind of bar of chocolate in fact, being honest, I don't eat them.

Is it a diet like?

Aye. Thanks for the coffee but.

That's alright.

You're no offended?

Naw. I'll eat it myself. On second thoughts I'll no, I'll keep it for later. He stuck it back into his pocket and studied the screen while sipping the coffee which was far too milky it was like water. Funny, how they said something was coffee and then sold you a cup of fucking water with just a splash – a toty wee splash – of brown stuff, to kid you on. Total con. They did the selfsame thing with tea, they charged you for tea but served you with milk and sugar and another wee splash of brown, a different tasting one. You couldn't trust them. But it was hard to trust people anyway, even at the best of times. You were actually daft if you trusted them at all. At any time. How could you? You couldn't. Cause they aye turned round and fucked you in some way or another. That was his experience.

The film would soon be done, thank God. It was a murder picture, it was about a guy that was a mass-murderer, he kills all sorts of folk. A good-looking fellow too, handsome, then he goes bad and starts all the killing, women mainly, except for a couple of guys that get in his way, security men in the hostel, it was a nurses' hostel, full of women, and a lot of them fancy him, the guy, the murderer, he gets off with them first, screws them, then after he's screwed them he kills them – terrible. And no pity at all.

But sometimes you could feel like murdering somebody yourself in a way, because people were so fucking awful at times, you helped them out and nothing happened, they just turned round and didn't thank you, just took it like it was their due. His landlord was like that, the guy that owned the house he stayed in, he was a foreigner, sometimes you helped him out and he didn't even thank you, just looked at you like you were a piece of shite, like you were supposed to do it because you stayed in one of his fucking bedsits, as if it were part of your fucking rent or something.

He was sick of the coffee, he leaned to place the carton on the floor beneath the seat. He grimaced at the woman. She didn't notice, being engrossed in the picture. To look at her now you would hardly credit she had been greeting her eyes out quarter-of-an-hour ago. Incredible, the way some females greet, they turn it off and turn it on. He was going straight home, straight fucking home, to make the tea, that was what he was going to fucking do, right fucking now. Hamburger and potatoes and beans or something, chips. He was starving. He had been sitting here for two hours and it was fucking hopeless, you weren't able to concentrate. You came to the pictures nowadays and you couldn't even get concentrating on the thing on the screen because

because it wasn't worth watching, that was the basic fact, because something in it usually went wrong, it turned out wrong, and so you wound up you just sat thinking about your life for fuck sake and then you started feeling like pressing the destruct button everything was so bad. No wonder she had been fucking greeting. It was probably just cause she was feeling so fucking awful depressed. About nothing in particular. You didn't have to feel depressed about something, no in particular, because there was so much of it.

The bar of chocolate in his pocket. Maybe he should just eat it himself for God's sake! He shook his head, grinning; sometimes he was a fucking numbskull. Imagine but, when he was a boy, leaving all these dowps lying vertical like that, just so somebody passing by would think they had landed that way! It was funny being a wean, you did these stupid things. And you never for one minute thought life would turn out the way it did. You never for example thought you would be sitting in the pictures waiting for the afternoon matinee to finish so you could go fucking home to make your tea, to a bedsitter as well. You would've thought for one thing that you'd have had a lassie to do it for you, a wife maybe, cause that's the way things are supposed to be. That was the way life was supposed to behave. When you were a boy anyway. You knew better once you got older. But what about lassies? Lassies were just so totally different. You just never fucking knew with them. You never knew what they thought, what they ever expected. They always expected things to happen and you never knew what it was, these things they expected, you were supposed to do.

What age was she? Older than him anyway, maybe 30, 35. Maybe even younger but it was hard to tell. She would've had a hard life. Definitely. Okay but everybody has a hard life. And she was on a diet. Most females are on a diet. She wasn't wearing a hat. Most females were these days, they were wearing hats, they seemed to be, even young lassies, they seemed to be as well; it was the fashion.

The more he thought about it the more he started thinking she might be on the game, a prostitute. He glanced at her out the side of his eye. It was definitely possible. She was good-looking and she was a bit hard, a bit tough, she was probably wearing a lot of make-up. Mostly females wore make-up so you couldn't really count that. What else? Did she have on a ring? Aye, and quite a few, different ones, on her different fingers. She shall have music wherever she goes. Rings on her fingers and rings on her toes. Bells on her toes. She had black hair, or maybe it was just dark, it was hard to see properly because of the light; and her eyebrows went in a high curve. Maybe she *was* on the game and she had got a hard time from a punter, or else somebody was pimping for her and had gave her a doing, or else telt her he was going to give her one later, if she didn't do the business, if she didn't go out and make a few quid. Maybe her face was bruised. Maybe she had got a right kicking. And she wouldn't have been able to fight back, because she was a woman and wasn't strong enough, she wasn't powerful enough, she would just have to take it, to do it, what she was telt, to just do it. God Almighty. It was like a form of living hell. Men should go on the game to find out what like it was, a form of living hell – that's what it was like. He should know, when he was a boy he had once went with a man for money and it was a horror, a horror story. Except it was real. He had just needed the dough and he knew about how to do it down the amusements, and he had went and fucking done it and that was that. But it was bad, a horror, a living hell. Getting gripped by the wrist so hard you couldn't have got away, but making it look like it was natural, like he was your da maybe, marching you into the toilet, the public toilet. Getting marched into the public toilet. People seeing you as well, other guys, them seeing you and you feeling like they knew, it was obvious, him marching you like that, the way he was marching you. Then the cubicle door shut and he was trapped, and it was so bad it was like a horror story except it was real, a living hell, because he could have done anything and you couldn't have stopped him because he was a man and he was strong and you were just a boy, nothing, to him you were just nothing. And you couldn't shout or fucking do anything about it really either because

because you were no just fucking feart you were in it along with him, you were, you were in cahoots, you were in cahoots with the guy, that was what it was, the bad fucking bit, you were in cahoots with him, it was like you had made a bargain, so that was that. But him gripping you the way he was! What a grip! So you had to just submit, what else could you do. You had to just submit, you couldn't scream nor fuck all. Nothing like that. Men coming into the urinals for a pish, no knowing what was going on behind the door and him breathing on you and feeling you up, and grabbing you hard, no even soft, no even caring if he had tore your clothes. What the wonder was that nobody could hear either because of the rustling noises the way he had you pressed against the wall and then you having to do it to him, to wank him, him forcing your hand and it was like suffocating him forcing his chest against your face and then coming over you, no even telling you or moving so you could avoid it it was just no fair at all, all over your shirt and trousers, it was terrible, a horror story, because after he went away you had to clean it all up and it wouldn't wipe off properly, all the stains, the way it had sunk in and it was like glue all glistening, having to go home on the subway with it: broad daylight.

For a pile of loose change as well. How much was it again? No even a pound, 50 stupid pence or something, ten bob. Probably no even that, probably it was something like 40 pee, he just stuck it into your hand, some loose change. What did prostitutes get? What did they get? Women, back then, nine year ago. It was probably about five quid if it was a short time; a tenner maybe if it was all night. That was enough to make anybody greet. But you could spend your life greeting, like his fucking sister. Because that was the thing about it, about life, it was pathetic, you felt like pressing the destruct button all the time, you kept seeing all these people, ones like the woman, the old dear at the end of the row, plus even himself as a boy, you had to even feel sorry for yourself, yourfuckingself. What a fucking joke. A comedy. Life was a comedy for nearly everybody in the world. You could actually sympathise with that guy up on the screen. You could, you could sympathise with him. And he was a mass-murderer.

He glanced at the woman along the row and smiled at her, but then he frowned, he glared. You shouldn't be sympathising with a mass-murderer. You shouldn't. That was the fucking director's fault. That happened in his pictures, you started feeling sympathy for fucking murderers. How come it wasn't for the victims. They were the ones that needed it. No the actual perpetrators. That was probably how she had been greeting, the woman, because of the fucking victims, she was a victim, and that's who it was happening to, the fucking victims. He wanted to go home, right now, he wanted out of it, right fucking out of it right fucking now it was a free country and he wanted to get away home for his fucking tea. He glanced along at her, to see what she was doing. She was still holding the carton of coffee, engrossed in the picture. The old dear as well. It was just him. He was the only one that couldn't concentrate. That was that nowadays, how he never seemed able to concentrate, it never fucking seemed to work any more, you couldn't blank it out. He kicked his coffee over. It was a mistake. But he was glad he had done it. He wished they had all fucking seen; it would sort them out, wondering how come he had done it, if it was meant; he got up off the chair and edged his way along to the end of the row, watching he didn't bump into her as he went, she never so much as glanced at him, then the old dear moving her bags to let him pass, giving him a look as he went, fuck her, even if he stood on one of them with eggs in it, bastard, he just felt so fucking bad, so fucking bad.

TONI DAVIDSON

TONI DAVIDSON

reasons and rhymes

Esler tickled the eczema patches on his hands and closed his eyes. His fingertips circled the reddened, wrinkled knuckles pausing briefly to let the sensation build before scratching with his jagged nails. He let his fingers trail halfway down his forearm where the next patch urged him to tease and tickle, scratch and burn . . . It was an old ritual, an insistent methodology. He had clawed his way through childhood, waking his parents in the night, staining his sheets with bloody skids, rubbing and kneading his skin trying to erase the persistent burn. Eventually he had been given cream and tight fitting white gloves so that his nocturnal scratching would be less damaging and less disruptive. In the middle of the night he felt like a slicked magician, waving his hands against the night light, conjuring up a new skin. There was always an upside however and when the urge to tickle and scratch diminished he would hold his hands close to his face, the bare funky knuckles pressed to his nose and close his eyes, inhaling himself with pleasure. No amount of hydro-cortezone could relieve his condition as much as that blissful event.

He was caught in reflection when he opened his eyes. His eyes flickered from an old man to a young girl before they settled on a young man opposite him. A ragged student, Esler guessed, thin-boned, deep-set eyes and uncomfortable with a stranger's gaze. He shifted awkwardly in his seat, turning more towards the window. Esler ignored the young man's discomfort and kept looking while he casually lowered his head. He knew how it looked. Someone who had seen him sniffing had commented, 'I though you were kissing yourself.'

Since he couldn't have the scent next to him he held it in his nose inhaling it like smoke, drawing it into his body . . .

WITHOUT YOU I AM NOTHING

Esler read the table graffiti and immediately wanted to add something to it. He felt in a playful mood. His ex-friends would shut down conversations, close the roads he might travel just to avoid his playful moods. *He's okay but when he gets a drink in him . . .?* More times than he could remember as a child his brother had run crying from their room, a game too far, a tease or a leg pull that had crossed some brotherly boundary. *He never wanted to be a dull boy Jack, you hear me . . .?*

He didn't mean for that to be said out loud. The old man and the young girl looked over at him. He didn't care. His parents had been given a name by a doctor for his inappropriate verbal expressions but he couldn't remember what it was. A teacher had said that he should stop saying what he thinks but that to him had never been sound advice especially in a school context. Speak up or get trampled would have been better advice. A smile drifted across his face as he stared out the old man who shook his head as he returned to his paper. And then there was the famous incident with a now dead aunt when she asked him how she looked in her new dress . . .

He searched for a pen feeling the need to reply to the message scrawled onto the table. Maybe it was a message from the young man who had hastily written the words when Esler had closed his eyes, lost to scent. This was a good working theory he decided, especially since the graffiti looked fresh and untarnished. The young man had covered up the message but, teasingly, only just enough and when the train tilted slightly the words were revealed. It was a message. Of course it was a message. Why not? It was going to be a long trip. The two of them had an intuitive bond. It was in the eyes and in the scent. They both knew the game and who was to see? An old man and a young girl whose mother was lost to some book? No one would witness or understand their actions. The best thing about the words was that they could be anything, would be anything. They were a level playing field. Forget crass attempts at conversation. The message was to the point.

Think, please Esler, before you speak.

This time the old man didn't look around and the young girl had shut her eyes. The words hung, unchallenged, in the air. Finding a pen, he wrote, pressing hard into the vinyl covering,

ᴉ ʙᴇʟᴉᴇᴠᴇ ʎoᴜ

The young man's stare was still directed out of the window, the landscape seemingly captivating. When he had finished the last word he used the magazine to conceal most of it. This was the game. Tit for tat, love for love. Esler could see it all and pleased with himself he brought his hand back up to his face and shut his eyes for a moment and allowed his intuition, his imagination to unravel.

He wanted the contact more than anything. It seemed like a long time since he had last fraternised with the anonymous; the adrenaline rush of risk and refusal, of a chance taken, of an opportunity engaged. If he had hands enough he would count the number of times he had wasted chances and opportunities. His recall was good, too good. In his mind he had catalogued refusals rather than celebrated successes. *In retrospect* was a clarion call he didn't want. Its purpose was dull and deficient. Spontaneity it seemed to him was an art that had to be learned.

Esler felt himself slip into the torpor of dilema where the mind is so active it forgets to let the body know that it must engage, that it must do more than simply exist. He opened his eyes and followed the young man's gaze first to the table and then to him. Esler felt a cold shiver work its way down then back up his spine while at the same time his skin flushed with fright. *They had connected!* This was the first step, the first move and soon they would empty the carriage with their outrageous behaviour, they would devour each other in full view of their fellow passengers. It was all set out to the point that Esler wondered where they would go from there, as they rested in each other's arms . . . Would he settle for just that or would this be the answer to the *so how did you guys meet* question they would have to answer for the rest of their lives. Even the train couldn't keep up with Esler's imagination.

Esler waited. The young man was playing coy. He was pretending now that it wasn't him who had scrawled the words on to the table and that his gaze catching Esler's reply was coincidence and nothing more than the roving eye of a bored passenger. But there was foot connection under the table! Was it coincidence too that they had just happened to touch not once or twice but three times, each time when Esler had his eyes shut, his hand pressed against his nose.

He hated this. Suddenly the young man exuded a calm that Esler did not believe. As he stared at the young man, using his eyes as weapons, he imagined violence against him, a cut across his pale white skin, a punch that dislodged a tooth or two and then, *then* he would twist his neck around forcing him to face Esler, and the truth. The countryside was nothing, Esler thought, there is nothing there that has not been seen before. I, on the other hand . . .

Esler could feel the seething anger unhinge his control. He was suddenly restless, his arms not finding a place they could rest comfortably; his head feeling loose as though his neck had ceased to support its weight. He recognised these signs. He had been told to keep himself under control so many times in his life; from parents to teachers; from passing adults appalled at his behaviour to colleagues spurning his every attempt to get on with his life. His attitude had been described as bad, twisted, fucked up and unhappy. He wore labels with pride. He had not met anyone in his life that understood him and that as far as he was concerned was their mistake. All around him he saw compromise being made because people had got lonely and desperate and though he yearned for contact, it wouldn't and shouldn't be at any price.

They went through a tunnel, close to the next station, and their reflected stares met disembodied somewhere in the black outside the train, hanging impossibly in some sooty limbo. There was no curiosity in the young man's eyes now and Esler found it hard to take, hard to believe. With a rapidly sinking heart and a rising temper he watched the young man put on his jacket and gather up his bag. As the train emerged from the tunnel he stood up, awkwardly trying to untangle himself from the small space between table and chair. Esler grabbed the pen and started to write on to the table, whilst he shouted, 'Look!' Shocked, the young man stumbled back against the seats while the old man and the young girl looked over at Esler whose pen was bending as he forced the nib down hard into the table.

I NEED YOU

The young man looked startled and staggered into the corridor. He tripped over someone's case and by half-running, half-jumping he managed to stop himself from falling and by then he was near the exit and in a moment he was gone.

Esler looked at the words he had etched into the table and wondered what he'd done wrong, why the young man should at first be so welcoming, so silently sensual and then turn so cold. He raised his hand to his face and breathed in his scent, searching with his nose for the exact spot on knuckles that exuded the most pungent smell. He shut his eyes and with his other hand he followed the letters of their communication with the tips of his fingers.

a bewitched embrace

DILYS ROSE

DILYS ROSE

Our throats were dusty, our eyes screwed against the glare. We didn't speak. We were not speaking. We had not been speaking for 70 or 80 kilometres, since the last village, a pretty place with broad-leaved trees, flowering creepers and at least two roadside restaurants. You'd wanted to stop there, let the car cool down, stretch your legs. I was keen to push on, cover more ground. As I was driving, I got my way. The car clearly sided with you.

The lake, if it was one, was a poisonous green, the ravaged ground rust red. In every sense it was an unnatural landscape, a gouged-out hillside, a cavity, bare of any vegetation other than whatever mutant matter occupied the water. That was where the car failed to make yet another of the steep inclines I'd been pushing it over for the last hour and ground to a halt, accompanied by the choking stink of burnt rubber. It was the hottest time of the day and the sun bit into our necks and bare shoulders as we abandoned our smoking old banger and made for the village, the shade and – *Please, please* – a cold drink.

We were the only customers in the only bar. The peeling walls were adorned with a greasy saint and a dog-eared calendar featuring a team photo of Real Madrid. There was no sign of the proprietor. If we'd

143

been speaking, you'd have reminded me of how nice the place we passed an hour before had looked, adding that there, even with a broken-down car, we might have enjoyed our stop instead of enduring it, that holidays were meant to be about enjoyment, not endurance. I know this would have been your line: we'd had this conversation/discussion/argument/falling out before. They say, people say, people who do research into people – how they get on and don't get on, how they leap together like magnets or whirl apart like magnets – they say that your first argument is the one you go on having.

I was thinking about this when a woman in her sixties emerged from a dark doorway behind the bar. Dyed black hair, too much kohl and lipstick, tight skirt and high, scuffed heels, she blinked like a night creature hauled from the shadows and stunned by daylight. Without a word she opened our bottles, dropped our coins into the till and retired to her private darkness, leaving us to tepid limonada, a rickety table and a squad of fat, buzzing flies. Outside, the dazed, empty street simmered in the afternoon haze.

A dog wandered in, sniffed around our legs. You patted its matted head, let it lick your damp, salty knees. I pushed it away. I didn't kick it, I nudged it with my foot. It could easily have been the other way round. Neither of us was a consistently committed animal lover. We didn't drool over fluffy puppies or cute kittens, just each other, though by then that too was becoming less consistently committed. As for the patting or pushing away, it could have been the other way round: it could have been me as Kind Princess and you as Hag. I didn't say this. We were still not talking. We were postponing talking for at least as long as the limonada lasted. A wilderness lacking any picturesque connotations of the word, a valley gutted by open-cast mining with a one-street, one-bar village tacked on, wasn't the best place to break down. But enjoyment wasn't the point and, if we'd been talking, I'd have said we could have done a lot worse. On that road, we could have easily broken down with nothing in sight but flayed, mineral-rich earth. And soon we'd be gone. By the time we finished our drinks and walked back up the hill, the engine and the radiator would have cooled down. I'd fill up the radiator with water – as driver, the radiator, engine, brakes, clutch and windscreen wipers were my responsibility – I'd turn on the ignition and our miraculous old car would once again revive. We'd continue on our way and, after a couple of hours, reach our destination in good enough time. As we roared up and down the switchback road, leaving the blasted landscape behind, we'd begin to look forward to the cabin we'd booked ahead months back: *Situated in pinewoods, our cabanas offer peace, seclusion and close encounters with nature. If that is not enough, a short walk brings you to our exclusive leisure complex: two pools, two restaurants, tennis courts, horse-riding, squash and mini-golf.*

Amazing: I'd memorised the blurb from the brochure. Well, maybe not so amazing. I'd quoted it so often over the winter months, chanted it like a spell to get us through the dark and cold, the flus and blues, the electricity meter popping coins like a Royal Mint junkie. *Close encounters with nature* made you giggle in that sexy, throaty way which made me want to get you there immediately. Indoors, especially in winter, you were modest and self-conscious in a way I found frustrating but outdoors you were a changeling. Outdoors turned you on, pinewoods in particular: the tang of conifers, sunlight slicing through deep green spears, the glisten of oozing, honey-coloured sap. Why else would I have agreed to such a long drive? Or you. Once we got going, you'd start to imagine the woods and we'd stop not speaking. Once we got going, the deadlock would be broken.

It was late afternoon by the time the breakdown lorry arrived, hoisted our dead car onto the trailer and delivered it, and us, to the garage where the only mechanic this side of the sierra shook his head, rolled his eyes and demonstrated the magnitude of our problem by throwing out his arms like a fisherman extolling *the one that got away*. With the help of the phrase book and frequent repetition of key words like *radiator*, *embrague*, *kaput* and *manana*, we began to get some sense of what was wrong with the car. *Embrague* stumped me at first. I thought our man with the ridged forehead, steely halo of curls and oil black hands had said *embruje* which, according to my phrase book, meant 'bewitched'. The car had been bewitched by the poison lake, drugged by toxins, put to sleep by the heat. It needed dark and quiet and the love of a stranger to bring it back to life. When the mechanic pulled out the clutch disc as proof of our problem, it was as smooth as a CD, the bite entirely worn away.

We left the car keys at the garage and went in search of a room for the night. Even still, the *embruje/embrague* confusion hung around in my head. It was something to think about as we sulked and slogged down the hot road to the hot village while our secluded cabana was waiting for us, nestling in cool, scented woods, out of reach. *Embruje*: bewitched. *Embrague*: clutch, grasp, embrace. A bewitched embrace. Lovers clinched for a lifetime, a century, eternity. I'd have asked you how you fancied that, you and me fused together for an unimaginable length of time but as we were only communicating via essential, clipped questions and grunted replies, I didn't.

Though siesta time was over the village hadn't exactly brushed the sleep from its eyes, opened its doors and stepped out to greet the world on its only street. Still, we had an address. Above an open door, daubed on the wall: 22.

'My favourite number,' you said once, long ago, adding, 'Like the two of us curled up for sleep.'

In the doorway, a girl in a flouncy red and white dress squatted on the steps like a crushed Christmas cracker. With a stick, she poked at a beetle floundering on its back, unable to right itself. I asked about the room. You said something complimentary and insincere about the little tyrant's dress. Then you tried to persuade her to turn the poor thing over. You were definitely Kind Princess that day, patting a mangy dog and worrying about a beetle. Slowly, the girl looked us up and down. Eyes round and deep as straws, she sucked in our cropped hair, sweat-soaked vests, our bare legs. When she'd drunk us in down to our hiking boots, she patted the red bow in her hair and ran off to fetch her mother.

Our situation was so predictable, the premise for any number of movie plots. Car breaks down. Travellers stranded in strange place. Strange people. Strange goings on. The scenario as old as the hills. Chiller or heart-warming comedy. In the chiller, the travellers inevitably become prey to some inbred, prejudiced weirdos. In the comedy, after being treated as outcasts, they win through, transforming some inbred prejudiced weirdos into warm-hearted human beings. There was a movie we watched together – remember? – about a bunch of New York drag queens who set off for California and, en route, solve the social problems of some mid-west town. My favourite lines from it were spoken by a maltreated but finally empowered wife to the leading queen, 'Soon as ah set eyes on you ah knowed you weren't no gel. A gel ain't got no Aidam's apple.' Something like that. Don't quote me.

Had we been getting on we might have taken up the challenge of trying to transform our avaricious landlady and her dour, overdressed daughter but this wasn't a movie and a plot line to push things on a bit, to drag us out of our own doldrums, didn't materialise. Nor did the *ventilador* we were promised to temper the air in our sweltering, overpriced boxroom. We'd thought about bringing the tent along in case something like this happened but where would we have pitched it? By the poison lake in the middle of a quarry?

We almost cancelled the holiday. We should have. I can see that now but hindsight's a fat lot of use and I can't even say you pushed for us to go because you didn't. I pushed for us to go and I pushed the damn car over one too many hills. I always was pushy. Which you liked, at first. I wanted to get there, to arrive, to reach the woods where you'd rub the pine needles against your skin until they shot out their green scent, where you'd throw river water in my face and catch droplets on your tongue as they splashed off me. I wanted to get there. Whoever said that the travelling and not the destination is all, is a fool.

We almost cancelled because, unlike many defunct industrial sites, the vast open-cast mine up the road would not have been recycled as a museum. Unemployed miners would not be retrained as tour guides. Not long after we booked our holiday and immediately before the mine closed down, its reputation as a danger to public health greatly outweighed share values: toxic waste broke its bins and flooded into the river, killing everything in it, in the fields fed by it and the wildlife sanctuary through which it flowed to the sea. The disaster made the international press. Worried, you brought me the newspaper article, and the map. The map was bigger than the kitchen table and drooped over the edge like a crisply pressed tablecloth we never wanted and never had. Between your thumb and index finger lay the black spot and the beauty spot.

'They're close on the map,' I said. 'But think of the scale.'

'I am. This is a big-scale disaster. It must be.'

'Maybe there was nothing else to put in the papers today. Maybe the editor's got a bee in his bonnet about toxic waste. Maybe it's World Ecology Week.' Like I said, I wanted to get there.

'It's the only piece about ecology.'

'Maybe there's a series: one a day for a week. A month. A year. A worldwide survey. Maybe we'll find we've a toxic waste problem on our own doorstep.'

Maybe: lifebelt for a drowning woman.

'I'm going to call the Foreign Office,' you said. 'Travel Help desk. They have one.'

Why do I remember that entire conversation when I can't remember what we said the last time we were together? As it was, I phoned the Travel Desk, to settle it, to put your mind at rest. I looked up the number in your address book and found it under 'H' for Help. And no, I wasn't side-tracked into combing the pages for unfamiliar names or enigmatic entries. The brisk, tight-lipped chap on the other end of the phone issued the official statement, 'We have no information on the area in question.'

'Any advice, then?'

'We have no information on the area.'

We got to know that hot room very well, the black constellations of dead mosquitoes on the flaky walls, the convoy of ants on the floor commandeering our crumbs of dry bread and sour, oily cheese. We also got to know each other too well, in the way cellmates or people confined in a small hospital ward get to know each other; obliged to share every breath, blink, sigh, cough, sniff, chew, swallow, scratch, rumble, belch, fart, snort, snore. After such relentless intimacy, desire hid beneath the beds.

Endurance was not the point of a holiday but endurance was our only option while the embrague was being replaced and the part for the radiator delivered from the other end of the country, apparently by donkey. Though we were lucky to have a room between us, separate rooms might have saved us. The landlady's preference for loud TV quiz shows didn't help, nor did her daughter's skulking around outside our door, eyes and ears to the keyhole – when did that child sleep? But the place and the people are blameless and irrelevant. The village shrank to the room. The room shrank to our bodies, on separate beds.

The heat was an enemy. If it had been cool or, better still, cold, at least we might have cuddled up for the sake of warmth. Instead, we sizzled and spat night after night, cooking in our own juices, the proximity of our bodies bearing no relation to closeness. Those slow hours, every day a replay of the one before – I have difficulty distinguishing them now. Other than the pre-breakfast trail to the garage, to hear yet another sincere apology from the mechanic, there was nothing to do but eat, drink, read, doze and blister with discontent. By the time the car was repaired, our money was gone, our cabana had been rented to a couple of cyclists and we were a lot further apart than just not speaking. I blame the lake.

from

BILL DOUGLAS

my way home

They wander along the sand between the two billets, a feeling of total lethargy in the air. It is reflected in the way Jamie is measuring the sand with his feet and in the kind of dislocated way Robert is moving. And this is how they are, one stopping, the other starting, sometimes separate, sometimes together, walking, standing.

Finally, the two of them are just standing there. Robert is gazing off in one direction, Jamie off in another. In a little while, unbeknown to Robert, Jamie will look at him, perhaps really studying him for the first time, then away again to appear as if he was thinking about something else. And eventually, Robert will do the same with Jamie, only this time Jamie will feel the look and turn. And they will both express the hint of a smile before turning away again to look at the sand.

Suddenly, Robert is pelting down the sand like some maniac let loose.

> *Robert*
> Watch out!

He swiftly approaches Jamie, who is in position for leap-frog and flattens him to a heap. Robert laughs and his laughter is a kind of helpless thing as if he knows life to be the most marvellous thing. Suddenly, he springs to his feet, gathering Jamie.

> *Robert*
> Come on, be alive, be alive, be alive, be alive!

He swings Jamie like a merry-go-round.

> *Robert*
> This'll put some life into you.

With that he dumps him.

> *Robert*
> Can't catch me.

But Jamie is immediately up and away in pursuit of the zig-zagging Robert, and there they are for all the world to see like two kids at the seaside.

> *Robert*
> He's alive. He is alive!

Robert is lying on the sand, reading a book. Jamie is doing nothing, just lying flat on his back. He breaks the silence.

> *Jamie*
> I don't think I like people.

Robert finishes his sentence before looking up. He goes back to his book.

> *Robert*
> Thanks.

Jamie glances round at Robert.

> *Jamie*
> I don't mean you.

He turns back to consider the sky again.

> *Robert*
> Well, that's nice to know.

He reads for a bit, then turns to study Jamie.

> *Robert*
> Anyway, people are all right.
> *Jamie*
> I want to do something.

Robert sighs, closes the book, tosses it down.

They are walking along the sand close to the barbed wire. Robert is seen to be lagging behind. He looks remarkably bored, sauntering here, sauntering there. Then he takes up a stance to watch Jamie, who has meanwhile turned to watch him. They are like statues.

Robert raises his arm and lets it flag against his thigh in an effort to express his feelings about the aimlessness of it all.

Jamie turns aimlessly away.

Robert crouches to the sand to watch an insect slowly wending its way.

It is while he is watching this that the sound of the plane comes. He rises to listen to the engine revving up, then the sound of it like a long-held sigh.

Then the charge of it along the runway and into the sky, disappearing.

Robert watches long after it has gone. Then, moving off, he confronts the waiting Jamie.

> *Robert*
> C'mon, you. I thought we were going to be doing
> something.

No reaction from Jamie. Robert looks irritable.

> *Robert*
> Come on!
> *Jamie*
> Don't you like walking?
> *Robert*
> We've walked.

Jamie thinks.

> *Jamie*
> Well, let's talk then.
> *Robert*
> What about if it isn't you?

There is a hint of a smile on Jamie's face.

> *Jamie*
> Well, let's go to the pictures then.
> *Robert*
> We've seen it.

Silence. Robert now gives up, turns away, disappears. Jamie follows.
They are walking along behind the barbed wire. Robert turns to

walk backwards. When finally he stops, Jamie stops.

> *Robert*
> C'mon now, what we want is one constructive
> idea.
> *Jamie*
> Can you think of something?
> *Robert*
> No, it should come from you for a change.

But nothing comes.
Robert begins to back away.

> *Robert*
> Look, I'll see you later, okay?

With that he turns and goes.

Jamie is at his bed space in the billet. His open locker door has
pictures of Marilyn Monroe hanging on it. He rummages inside for
his uniform.

The fans on the ceiling are making whirring sounds in an
otherwise silent place.

Robert is sitting on the edge of a bed putting Duraglit to his
buttons. This is his space in the billet. On the wall surrounding him
– he occupies a corner bed – hang pictures of Eisenstein and Sibelius.
There is also a picture of a skull divided up into different
compartments like rooms in a house. His bedside table is piled with
books. Jamie dumps his uniform on the bed and sits down beside
him. Then he turns his gaze to the pile of books and says:

> *Jamie*
> What a lot of books you've got.

Robert doesn't look up, just answers.

>   *Robert*
>   I've got a lot more at home.

Jamie takes one of the books, turns it about for a bit and puts it back.

Robert hands the jacket over to Jamie, who proceeds to wipe off the Duraglit. They remain in silence just cleaning away.

Robert is lying on the sand on his back, this time reading another book. Jamie is again sitting there doing nothing. He looks bored. He shovels up a handful of sand and lets it slip through his fingers. He glances at Robert but there is nothing doing there. He lies back on the sand but a moment later is shooting up again. He sighs. His voice when it comes seems to ache from boredom.

>   *Jamie*
>   Do you want to do something?

Robert, an enclosed isolated face lost in his reading. He lets out a brief laugh, then is silent again.

>   *Jamie*
>   I'm bored.

Robert finishes his sentence before looking up. He considers Jamie for a moment then turns on his side. He moves his index finger to make a small cross in the sand.

>   *Robert*
>   Do you know what that is?

Jamie, an isolated face, looks puzzled.

Robert
That's you.

He pauses to let that sink in. Then he forms another cross about a foot distant.

Robert
That's me.

Robert's finger moves with forceful deliberation to draw a line separating the two crosses.
  Then picking up his book he goes.
  He crosses the sand, goes inside the billet, lets the door go.
  Jamie, an isolated figure, watching.
  Inside, Robert is lying quite still on his bed with his hands clasped together across his forehead, not a particularly happy face.

From the back of a jeep, we pass beside the line of painted bricks and out through the main gates where a large sign announces 'Royal Air Force Abu Sueir'.
  Jamie is a solitary figure in the back of the jeep, his body juddering in rhythm to the sound of the engine.
  The rhythm changes as the vehicle takes a curve into the town square and screeches to a halt.
  The cabin door slams shut, then there is a hint of the driver disappearing swiftly through a swing door.
  Jamie, a huddled sleeping face. He raises his hand to rub his eye with the back of his hand, the way a child does, then he lowers it to rest on his rifle.
  Sound of a child's voice pleading pathetically.

Boy
Faloos?

But Jamie is lost in the land of nod.

The voice comes again, a little more prominent.

> *Boy*
> Kateer faloos.

Jamie opens his eyes on a child in rags. He has his hand raised up. Now he moves it to his mouth to suggest taking in food. Then he picks up his vest to rub his stomach and back to his mouth again, before reaching up.

Jamie makes a hopeless gesture suggesting he hasn't got anything. He hears the boy say:

> *Boy*
> Money.

The boy simply extends his hand more.

Jamie has the insides of his pockets held out.

> *Jamie*
> I'm sorry, I've no money.

A mother and child in a hut like something out of a nativity.

Sounds of the engine revving up.

The boy's face breaks into a glorious smile and the once pleading hand becomes something that waves.

The vehicle draws Jamie away and he too is smiling and waving.

The boy becomes a small figure still waving.

The vehicle carrying Jamie looks small and insignificant. The landscape it is passing through is undisturbed except for a long single track as if left there by a phantom wheel. The jeep reaches the line, runs parallel with it for a time, then breaks through.

There is a group huddled in a circle in the middle of the billet floor.

from my way home **157**

In the centre, amongst the knees and plimsolls, there is a wriggling camel spider. A hand fetches a tin of paraffin and proceeds to pour a generous supply of liquid round the creature.

Jamie, a passive face, watching.

Another hand strikes a match, lowers it, leaves it suspended.

Jamie breaks away from the circle with its private ritual, and goes to join up with Robert, who is quietly ruling out a chart. When finally the private circle lets out a victorious yell and stampedes and slams the door, it is Robert who looks up. He goes back to his task. Then Jamie looks up.

> *Jamie*
> Can I borrow one of your books?

Robert doesn't bother to look up this time.

> *Robert*
> Help yourself.

Jamie picks up a book, opens it.

> *Jamie*
> Thanks.

He wanders off. Robert watches after him. Then he considers his chart. After the words TIME EX it has been blocked off into days. At the tail end it says HOME. His hand comes to fill in another box.

Then he turns to pin it up on the wall.

Jamie, turned away on his bed, enclosed, reading the book.

The spider is a charred mess on the floor.

> *Jamie*
> What're you doing?

He approaches Robert carrying yet another book in his hand. He sits on a ridge of sand. Robert has a pen poised in his hand.

> Robert
> Writing home.

He gives up, groans.

> Robert
> I can't think of anything to say. You're lucky.
> Jamie
> Why?
> Robert
> You don't have that problem.

Jamie thinks about it.

> Jamie
> I wouldn't mind.

Robert plonks the pad and pen on Jamie's lap.

> Robert
> Go on then, you write something.

Jamie puts the pad right back where it came from.

> Jamie
> I don't know your family.
> Robert
> Well, now's your chance.

He rips a sheet from the pad, makes Jamie take it. Then he is content to let the sand drift through his fingers.

Jamie begins to write a line or two. Then

> *Jamie*
> How many Ls are there in 'wonderful'? One or
> two?

Jamie comes yelling down the sand. He has a bayonet in his grasp.
   He thrusts it into a sawdust bag.

They are waiting outside the cinema next to the sign 'Q here'.
   They are in their usual manner of distraction. Jamie barely steals a glance at the not so oblivious Robert, but he in turn manages to study the other quite hard.
   We hear a plane taking off overhead.
   Jamie asks into space.

> *Jamie*
> What will you do when you get back?
> *Robert*
> I suppose I'll eventually go to university.

He turns.

> *Robert*
> How about you?
> *Jamie*
> I want to be an artist.

He turns to look at a poster for *Niagara*.
   He thinks hard for a moment. Then he turns adding:

> *Jamie*
> Maybe even a film director.

Robert's voice is a curious mixture of suspended belief and release at hearing something positive.

> Robert
> Wow!

Robert focuses his camera.

> Robert
> Say 'cheese'.

Jamie is posing in a galabea.

> Robert
> Smile!

And, we feel for the first time ever, Jamie smiles.

Cairo. At a table outside a coffee shop, Jamie and Robert are relaxing. An Arab boy brings Jamie a hookah and sets it up for him.

> Jamie
> Thank you.

Robert watches as Jamie tries this new experience.
   Later, the city street is full of activity, except for Robert and Jamie who are just standing around.

> Robert
> Okay, what shall we do now?
> Jamie
> I know a place we could go.

He fetches out a guidebook from his pocket, glances through it. Now he opens up the map to study that. During this, Robert is looking at Jamie in an amused way as much as to say, well, look at him! Jamie manoeuvres the map to get his bearings right.

Then he traces his finger along the route.

The place of interest is a mosque and there are many people going towards it, removing their shoes before they enter.

We hear the mullah calling.

Robert and Jamie come in to look around. They are separate for a moment, Jamie engrossed in his guidebook. Then Jamie comes to pull Robert,

> *Jamie*
> Hey, Robert. Look.

He points up.

They are small figures now against the mosaic. Merely a detail at first, it gradually opens up to become an all-enveloping complete thing.

Jamie is quietly packing his kit bag. He goes to his locker door where he screws up the Marilyn pin-ups but retains and pockets the last one. Then he looks off and he doesn't look too happy.

Robert is busy putting finishing touches to a map. Jamie dumps his bag and sits down.

> *Robert*
> Look, here's the way to get there.

He hands it to Jamie.

> *Robert*
> Put it in a safe place.

Jamie, an isolated face, studying the map.

> *Robert*
> If you feel like it, look us up sometime. There's no
> need to be shy.

He can hear Robert add

> *Robert*
> If you like, you can stay.

Then

> *Robert*
> If you want, you can call it home.

JOSEPH MILLS

JOSEPH MILLS

from

towards
the end

As usual I had two very quick whiskies when I reached the pub. There was so much tension to get out of my system: worry about leaving the house empty, guilty feelings about going behind Pat's back; anxiety about how I would react to Alex if he should pop in later. The first time I met him after I began going out alone again had been worse than expected. There was no way I could avoid being near him: I knew so few people on the gay scene that the only alternative to joining his company was standing alone a few feet away from him, like a fool. Besides, the main reasons I had began going out at all was to try to exorcise Alex from my consciousness, to live through that one last thing which would put an end to it all. Despite the fact that I felt so uncomfortable, I was determined to stick it out.

But the sight of Alex mooning over his new friend was unendurable. Watching them together, talking and joking in that exclusive language that only two people at any one time can understand, I felt the same sort of despair that a divorced parent must feel on seeing his only child clinging to its new parents. Despite everything that had happened, I still thought of Alex as mine and only mine.

Gradually, though, those encounters began to have less effect on me. Alex made attempts, every time I met him, to make me feel jealous or unsettled. This had the opposite effect on me: they only showed that, no matter how much attention he lavished on his new boyfriend (reaching new heights of Cartlandesque embarrassment, maintaining a kiss for ten minutes) he still couldn't take my presence for granted.

Alex hadn't arrived by ten o'clock that night, which meant that he wasn't going to be there: I could relax.

'Have you ever been in love?' I asked the so-so-looking man who had sidled up beside me and started a conversation. It was a question I had asked everybody I had gone home with, eager to discover in their experience some indication of what it was I felt for Alex and Pat, hopeful that someone could tell me which was most worth while.

Mark, the man I was talking to, was not very attractive, but bravely optimistic. His clothes were too stylish for his podgy frame: he was wearing a Labrador-yellow sweat shirt which screamed desperately and pathetically for attention, like advertising hyperbole on second-hand goods. He may as well have embroidered The Legendary Mark across his chest.

'God, does it show?' he replied in answer to my question. Luckily Mark was a brooder, a thinker and a talker. Some of the people I'd spoken to seemed to have drifted through life, from one crisis to another, without ever stopping to analyse their situation to help them avoid any traumas in the future. That type was no good to me. Mark had thought through his mistakes endlessly; his story came gushing out fluently and articulately.

I went along with him to the disco, an hour earlier than anyone else – at my insistence: I wanted the upper hand in the proceedings. I had become rather cynical about cruising since I had started going back out alone again. Getting in early allowed me to view everyone as they poured into the disco: I was able to study closely their various states of confidence or nervousness, as well as their physical attributes. Which was an Alex, which was a Pat – that was really what I was interested in.

I bumped into Sammy as Mark and I came off the dance floor later in the night. I had met him three weeks previously. The first words he had said to me were 'You must drink a lot of milk' while squeezing my, by then, firm rounded biceps. Sammy only drank in The Waterloo and was most definitely Rough.

'You're looking great,' he said to me that night, grabbing my crotch and peering into my eyes. Sammy was anything but subtle. I introduced him to Mark, but only after accepting his compliments and buttering him up a bit: he was dangerously slow and liable to explode into violence if not treated properly.

As Mark and he made a desultory conversation I began to look around the hall at all the faces, all the types, and it struck me how difficult it was going to be to become involved with anyone again: even the most mundane task of all – finding a body for the night was strewn with pitfalls. Finding a face that fitted the image of acceptability in the mind was only the first step: more often than not, the personality did not fit the face. Before I heard Sammy speak, as I watched him from afar that night I saw him in the disco, I had supposed him to be a lawyer or a doctor, due to the expensive-looking suit he wore, and his tidy appearance. It was only when he turned up a week later, in torn jeans and a dirty white T-shirt that I went home with him and found out he was a labourer: the suit was for a court appearance that day.

There were so many familiar faces now that it was strange to remember how, not so long ago, I had thought the Glasgow gay scene so big and unmanageable. All the regulars were there: Black Marilyn – androgynous Indian beauty (was it a girl or a guy?) in suit and tie; the man in his fifties who always danced by himself, swishing a red cape around as though he were taunting an imaginary bull; and the fashion queens, acting out all the videos to the pop songs blasting from the speakers, working so hard at enjoying themselves and looking cool (by the end of the night they would have rejected every potential partner with an icy stare, waiting for Mr Worthy-of-me, only to go home with the first person who asked – regardless of looks, age or intelligence – when the lights came up).

The fact that 'the scene' was small suited everybody: there was only ever one disco open at a time on any particular night, so no worries about what you might be missing elsewhere; and all the bars were within easy walking distance of each other. This meant that people drifted from one to another, often several times a night. The Waterloo, because it was on a busy shopping street and open to the sun, was busy early on in the day; when it got dark, people made their way to The Vintners and Squires. Because it was such a small collective of gay people that circulated round the pubs and discos it seemed to operate intuitively, like one huge organism: new establishments were flocked to and deserted en masse: transsexuals and transvestites always marginalised themselves (or were marginalised by everybody else) into the less reputable places; and there was only ever one lesbian bar at any particular time, because of the relatively smaller numbers. Although everyone always *said* they preferred mixed male/female (and most of the intelligent ones did), there was not much point in the women going to half a dozen places where they knew they would be outnumbered 20 to one when there was one place they knew all their friends would be; and the single males only ever went where 'the men' were.

Sammy was mocking the camper elements in the crowd. 'Look at them all in their best frocks,' he said disgustedly. I dragged him up to dance to the first camp record that came on: 'You Always Hurt the One You Love'.

'Shouldn't that be the other way round?' I said to him when we were on the dance floor. He looked over at the record spinning on the DJ's turntable. 'Will I make him turn it over?' he said.

'No. I mean the one you love always hurts you.' But he only started expressing that paranoid, confused look until I kissed it away.

When we returned to Mark, a man in his forties was talking to him. Immediately we came over, he broke off the conversation and began to back away. 'Well, I'll leave you young chaps alone. You don't want me cramping your style.'

'God, I hate that sort of self-pitying crap,' I said to Mark when the man had gone.

'Oh, Colin's got his problems,' Mark said. 'How would you feel if you came in here and you were his age.'

'He's only in his forties for God's sake.'

'How many guys is he going to get at that age in here, though?'

'But how many girls would he get if he were straight? Why is it gays blame every problem they have on being gay? If Colin were straight he would probably be married to a 40-year-old woman. Would he be any happier? Certainly not sexually.'

'Yes, perhaps we've come to expect too much from each other,' Mark said. Why is it that articulate liberalism is such a sexual turn-off? Since I didn't feel like having my cock chewed black and blue by Sammy that night, I slipped away while they were on the dance floor, embarrassed as always at the banal appropriateness of the Hi-Energy soundtrack to my exit ('Thank God, there's always tomorrow — because tonight my man's not here — oh no.').

On the way home, as usual when I was alone, I regretted that I didn't have a partner with me as I passed all the dishevelled sexuality of the similarly unlucky straight boys pouring out of the discos: all that sexual energy going to waste.

I passed a girl who was standing in the middle of the street with a vaguely solicitous look. I wondered if she was a prostitute. But as I got closer, I could see that she was waiting for her boyfriend, who was pissing in the street against a wall, his hot stream creating new continents on the map of vomit beside him, a landscape made three dimensional when he dropped a bag of chips onto it. The girl began to hiccup and I felt sick.

from

i love me (who do you love?)

GORDON LEGGE
GORDON LEGGE

Eddie lowered the phone. Shit, damn and blast.

Somebody had seen him getting off the bus. Said somebody had been telling another party about this when a bypasser happened to overhear the conversation, a bypasser that went by the name of Fids.

Oh God, Fids. Eddie had forgotten all about Fids. He'd never even thought about the guy, not once, not since the last time he'd seen him. Now he was going to have to spend time with this guy like he was some kind of mate or something. It was like seeing shit on your shoes, and then shit on the carpet, and then shit on the . . .

It had taken all of Eddie's powers of persuasion to prevent Fids from coming up to the game. Eddie emphasised the cost and Fids's poverty. Eddie also reminded Fids that Fids didn't like football, and how he wouldn't be wanting Fids to feel left out.

Fids had complied, he always did.

Eddie promised he would go round and see Fids on the Sunday afternoon. Eddie stressed this, that Eddie would go and see Fids. The last thing Eddie wanted was Fids turning up at his door. His folks would have a hairy fit.

Fids had hung up when his money ran out. Eddie was rather touched – the man who never had any money had spent his money phoning Eddie. Fids wasn't all bad. He was just too petty, pathetic, paranoid and poor, just like the town, so small-minded, all the things that had driven Eddie to seek his fame, fortune and happiness elsewhere.

Eddie went back up the stair and started getting himself the gether for going out. His old room was looking so much smaller these days. It reminded him more of all those hotel rooms he'd been in when he was away on courses. So neat and fresh and tidy was it that it came as something of a shock to see that the cupboard wasn't empty, but was filled with the neatly stacked remnants of a child and a teenager: shoeboxes full of pendants and postcards and photos and badges; some embarrassing LPs, a few tapes and most of his books.

Pride of place, though, went to a fort his dad had made for him, complete with inaccessible walkways cause the ladders had been broken off and used for something else. There was a poly-bag from the old pet shop filled with hatless and headless cowboys and Indians. Eddie's favourite was always the cowboy that had his hands tied behind his back. He was the one that won all the fights and did all the rescuing.

Eddie laughed. The other day he'd just been talking with someone about the relative merits of Sonic the Hedgehog and the toys of his generation. Sonic had won hands down, of course, but now Eddie wasn't so sure. There was something intensely personal about all this.

Eddie checked the time, it was getting on. He put everything back in the cupboard and got himself changed into his jeans and football top.

The top had prompted a few reactions down south, a few greetings, a few puzzled looks and more than a few sneers. One of the latter had come on the tube from a Jambo saddo who started haranguing Eddie about a dodgy penalty a few seasons back. They got to talking and the guy invited Eddie up to Hyde Park on the Sunday afternoon where a group of ex-pats challenged and thrashed all-comers from itinerant Australians to Rolls-Royce-driving Arabs.

Sounded all right to Eddie and he'd gone along and quickly established himself as a regular. One week they'd all played against a team from the Dorchester. Afterwards they'd all got the gether for a chat and a bev, and Eddie got talking to this boy called Simon, and, to cut a long story short, Simon had gone on to become Eddie's flatmate.

And that's what this trip was all about. This time he wasn't just going to use the word flatmate. Like he'd said flatmate about Brian at college and like he'd said flatmate about John through in Glasgow. That's all he ever told anybody. Everybody that was apart from his folks, who he'd told years ago, and who'd been pretty good about it, although his dad had said that if Simon was to visit it was to be separate rooms – he'd said it would have been the same if it was a girl. Eddie had also told Carol, shortly after telling his folks, half-hoping she'd tell everybody else. She hadn't, though; Carol liked her secrets.

Eddie pocketed his money and went back down the stair. He wanted to phone Simon but there was no news so he didn't. It was Simon that had told him he was to stop making a cunt of himself and to come up here to tell folk, to come out.

Eddie looked in on his folks before he left. They were curled up cosy on the settee, getting stuck into the box of Thornton's he'd got them, and watching a video of Daniel O'Donnell. Not since the heyday of Sydney Devine had his folks got so worked up about a singer. The living-room was a cross between a shrine and a warehouse: records, tapes, calendars, pendants, everything.

'Right,' said Eddie's mum, 'he's got a beautiful voice, a lovely voice. I like his songs, too. Aye, I like his songs. And he's got a wonderful personality, and oh he's just lovely. And, here,' Eddie's mum whispered, 'he's got a lovely wee bum.'

Eddie's mum and dad started giggling and cuddling up to each other.

On the screen Eddie got a glimpse of the tightly packed O'Donnell hind-end. Like two peas in a pod, as they said.

'Eddie! Fuck, man, what you playing at? Damn near gave us the fright of my life.'

'How come, gangsters after you or something?'

Eddie laughed but Graeme didn't. Some things were funny. Like pretending, however unwittingly, to be a black shell-suited, tattooed-knuckled, Regal-smoking famously psychotic bampot.

'Hey,' said Graeme, remembering what Eddie'd said, 'you're joking about that fire, eh?'

'Nah, he's a good player, always caused us a fair amount of problems.'

'Christ, if that's your criteria, you could sign half the cunts in the league. Come on, elephant man, let's see a few bastards getting their legs broken the night, right up to the armpits!'

'Eddie, come on to fuck, man.'

Eddie laughed. 'Gary coming the night?'

'Nah, it's just money, he says,' Graeme did his Gary impersonation, *'It's just money.'*

'Still the same, ih. Here, you wanting one of these?'

'Thought you were supposed to have stopped. Last time I seen you you said you'd stopped.'

'Aye, six months it lasted. Six months with waking up in the morning and dying for one, every single bastern morning was like that. So I just says to myself fuck it, and starts again.'

Graeme tutted. 'Should've stuck with it.'

'Nah, think about it, six months, man, never got any easier. Guys like us'll never stop.'

'Nah, Christ, I'm stopping,' said Graeme. 'Got it sussed.'

'Your arse, you'll never stop.'

Aye, I will said Graeme, but only to himself. Eddie was not the sort of smoker Graeme wanted to discuss this with. Eddie was too unrepentant, a failed giver-upper, as they were known. Graeme quickly changed the subject.

'Some support these cunts've brought up, eh?'

'Aye,' said Eddie, 'right shower of bruisers.'

'You seen this lot?'

'Aye, should take four of us easy. You still go to all the games?'

'Oh aye. Close thing last season, half of them could've went either way. Mind you, the other half were seriously shite.'

'Same old story. Funny, in Europe you've got all these crappy wee teams like Sampdoria winning the league but over here nothing ever changes.'

'One day it'll be different,' said Graeme.

'And you can nail jelly to the ceiling. You coming along to get slaughtered later?'

'Eh,' Graeme'd have to get fags. He'd have to buy 20, maybe 40. 'No,' said Graeme. 'No, I've got work the morrow. Early rise.'

'How's the job going?' said Eddie.

'All right, got promoted the day.'

'Aye? That you getting to use the scissors on the sellotape now?'

Graeme laughed. 'No quite that bad. Got a bit of a rise.'

'Should get yourself down south.'

Graeme pointed to the pitch.

'Sad bastard,' said Eddie. 'Hey, I thought you said Mr Smart-but-casual wasn't coming the night?'

Graeme looked across and, there, walking down the front so as he could get a good look at the WPCs behind the goal, was Gary.

'See his mam still buys his clothes, anyway,' said Eddie. 'Look at him, just look at the guy, he's staring right through that lassie. Watch it, watch it, here it comes!'

Eddie and Graeme burst out laughing as Gary nodded, winked and smiled at the two WPCs.

'Poor bastard,' said Graeme, 'still trying to convince the world he's no a poof.'

Eddie grimaced – that was what they called a sare yin.

Waiting.

Waiting for something to start then waiting for something to happen then waiting for something to finish.

Hazel checked the clock on the wall then the watch on her wrist. The clock was winning but there was ages yet so Hazel started on her second mat, peeling and picking at the corners, trying to separate the label from the cardboard. If she could manage it in a oner she'd be the new world champion.

Hazel was early cause Andy'd insisted they'd have to take the same bus up the town. It was one of those times when he'd got all manly and masterful, like it was one of the rules laid down by Andy's own personal Moses. Andy wouldn't hear of Hazel travelling up on her own, even with this daylight you couldn't be too careful. He'd even offered the ultimate sacrifice – taking the later bus, which would've suited Hazel but which would've meant Andy missing the start of the game. The way he'd swollen those doleful panda eyes of his had been rather touching. Bless him.

Nah, stuff him. Missing the start of the game wasn't what had been bothering him, it was the explanation he'd had to have given good old Dunky Dunx.

The label came off in a oner and Hazel rolled it as tight as she could, then rubbed it between her fingers, taking off all the sticky stuff and leaving a nice smooth surface.

Sound, that was what he'd said, it was sound. That was the new word – that was the worst, that was just the worst, that was worse than mates.

Hazel didn't like waiting, and she sure as hell didn't like waiting in public. One of the things about having a live-in boyfriend was you weren't supposed to do things like this anymore.

The label on the other side wasn't coming off so easy. Hazel wasn't going to get anything even remotely resembling a big bit. First round elimination. The disgrace of it. Hazel decided she would change the rules once she worked out what the new game was, in the meantime she would just pick it to bits, excavating with her nails then parting with her fingertips.

That Eddie bloke, that was worth some contemplation. She could while away some time thinking about how she was going to bring that up. Something between him and Carol.

'Hey, boys,' said Gary. 'Do you think if I sang "She's too sexy for the police" everybody would join in?'

Graeme said, 'No, please, please don't,' and took out his fags and gave one to Eddie.

'Andy's just out of order,' said Dunx. 'Just completely out of order. Acting like he's ashamed to be seen with us.'

'Speak for yourself,' said Eddie.

'Nah,' said Dunx, 'you know what it is? He's ashamed of himself, that's what it is. Watch him, look, he can't justify himself.'

'Would I be right in assuming you two've fallen out?' said Graeme. 'Just a guess, like.'

Dunx ignored him. 'It's all a sham, all this, that's all it is. It's all a sham. It's this woman, man. She is one major problem.'

'What the fuck is he havering about?' whispered Graeme to Eddie.

'Tell you later. You know what your trouble is, Dunky Dee. You are one jealous bitch.' Eddie gulped at his use of the word bitch.

'Fuck off,' said Dunx, 'I can't stand her.'

'Arsehole, I don't mean that, I mean you're jealous of her for taking away your wee bum chum.'

'Shite, Christ, your arse,' said Dunx. 'Hey, I'm going out with somebody, it's never affected the time I've had for my mates. Nah, she's manipulative that one, she's turning him against us.'

'Regardless, you're still a jealous bitch.' Eddie liked that word. 'Mind my going away day, you were giving it all your "Don't go, please stay, don't go, please stay".'

'Christ, I was pished, and anyway I'm not ashamed of that. We're your mates, we're your absolute best mates, you'll never take that away, I don't care how much you earn. You'll never have mates as good as us as long as you fucking live.'

Fucking pish, thought Eddie to himself, but never said anything.

'Go on,' said Dunx. 'Deny it, I dare you. D'you know what we're like? We're like women, man, we're like women.'

Eddie swallowed the biggest swallow of his life.

'Nah,' said Dunx, 'know how they always go on about how women are closer to each other than men are? Well, we're the crew, we're the generation, that disproves that cause everything we did, we did the gether.'

'I.e. fuck all,' said Graeme.

Andy checked his watch. Ninety seconds remained. He could sprint in 30. He just wanted one last act of defiance.

'Come on,' said Dunx, offering the 10p again. Dunx went over to the phone. 'Just pick it up, dial the numbers and say "Hello, Hazel, I'm having a really good time and I'm just staying over here. See you later. Bye." Simple as that. D'you want me to phone her for you? Right, I'll phone for you.'

Andy, though, went over and pushed Dunx away from the phone then walked over to the door.

'Right,' said Dunx, 'away you go then. Fuck off and away you go. But there's one thing, right, there's just one thing I want to say to you, just one thing. You listening? Well, listen to this, listen to this one then. You know what you are? D'you know what you fucking are? I know a lot about you mind and I know what you fucking are. You want to know what you are? Eh? Ih? You want to know? Well, I'll tell you . . . You are a fucking woman, that's what you fucking are. You're a fucking woman, a fucking wifie. That's all I've got to say on the matter, a fucking woman. On you go.'

Andy just shook his head and headed for the door.

'Just hold on a sec.'

Andy turned round cause it was Eddie who'd spoken.

Andy watched as Eddie climbed up on his chair then up on the table.

'Talking of being a fucking woman,' said Eddie. 'I have an announcement to make . . .'

'Yeah . . . A-ha . . . Yeah . . . Just like you wanted, standing on the table in a macho Scottish pub . . . I fucking did, ya wanker. Honest. Got half a ton of witnesses . . . Look, hold on a minute.' Eddie bunged in another couple of pound coins. 'Still there, aye? . . . Hey, guess what, though? This place is stowed with fucking Geordies . . . Stowed out, mobbed, packed . . . No, they're up for a pre-season . . . 7–3 . . . Them . . . No, nobody's said anything . . . But that's them told so everybody'll know . . . What's with all the questions, anyway? This the Simon inquisition, is it?'

While Eddie was on the phone, the folk at the table sat by their pints. Even though Baz, Wor Patrick, Wor Christine and Wor Stevie had only just arrived on the scene, they were waiting for Dunx to react like they'd known him all their lives.

'Crikey,' said Andy.

Dunx scowled. '"Crikey"?' he repeated. 'Fucking "crikey"? That's all you've got to fucking say for yourself. That is the entirety of what you've got to say. The cumulative effect of all your tiny brain cells, all beavering away and all ganging up the gether, the effect of all that has come away with the great philosophical observation "crikey". Fuck's sakes, man.' Dunx paused. 'This is a major as, this is a serious major as.'

They were all quiet for a few seconds until Baz said, 'Major as what, canny lad?'

Dunx scowled and it was left to Andy to explain. 'It's an expression,' said Andy, 'like as cool as or smart as. It's like the ultimate, the extreme. Not that I think that myself, of course.'

'Fuck off. Talk sense, will you?' said Dunx. 'Course it is, course it fucking is. Hey, remember that guy's showered with us, showered with us at five-a-side mind.'

'So what?' said Andy. 'Christ, everybody checks each other out, everybody sizes up.'

'That's different. Telling you, that was one thing he never did, he never sized up. Aye, too busy thinking about things, too busy fantasising. Aye, I've always had my suspicions about that bloke.'

Andy laughed. For Dunx to accept this would be a real major as – and Dunx was going to accept this because no one Andy knew of had ever exerted a greater influence over Dunx politics, tastes or humour than Eddie; a status Andy had long been jealous of.

from **i love me (who do you love?)**

Dunx never took anything from Andy, never agreed with anything Andy ever said or praised anything Andy ever did. Like anything new or different Andy ever said, bought or even laughed at was frowned upon by Dunx and made out to be an embarrassment by Dunx. Whereas if Eddie had been the source Dunx would be going, 'Aye, aye, aye, a-ha, aye, aye, aye.'

'Cannot believe it,' said Dunx, 'just cannot fucking believe it.'

'You're just after saying you've always had your suspicions,' said Wor Christine.

Dunx scowled at Wor Christine.

Andy laughed again. God, he was loving this, loving it all so much he wouldn't miss it for the world.

'It's not natural.'

'Your arse.'

'Is it Dan?' said Dunx. 'It is not fucking normal and that's the end of it.'

'What the fuck d'you mean by normal?'

'Jesus, normal's normal, it's what folk do.'

'Aye, you're just acting sideways cause I've never made a pass at you.'

'Aye, right. This is not funny, by the way. You're not Julian Clary, you're one of us.'

'One of what?'

'One of us, one of the lads. You're into the same stuff. You're into all the best of gear and all that. You go to the games. You're into good music.'

Eddie laughed. 'So?'

'So, so that's all, that's all I've got to say on the matter.'

'Can I still be your pal?'

'I don't know, I don't know about that. It's all about trust.' Dunx took a drink. 'What is this, anyway? I mean really what is all this all about? You been having women problems or something? It's all to do with Carol, eh?'

Eddie sighed. 'What you on about? Fuck all to do with Carol.'

'Aye, right. You and her were pretty close for a while there. Don't think I've forgotten. Don't think nobody noticed. Sneaking round when Deke wasn't there. You were fucking smitten, pal.'

'Listen, I was going through a bad spell, right. I confided a lot in Carol. Christ, this was eight years ago mind. I'd been dumped, right, and I needed someone to talk to. I had to see about some tests.'

'Tests?' Dunx looked puzzled. 'What, your exams, like? You were failing your exams so you went a wee bit sideyways?'

'No, not that kind of tests.'

Dunx got half-serious. 'You mean test tests?' Eddie nodded. 'This is serious,' Dunx slammed his drink down, 'this is fucking serious. It's fucking sordid all this, it's fucking sordid.'

'How's it fucking sordid?'

'Cause it is. It's not natural.'

'That's just fear talking.'

'Exactly, too damn right it's fear talking. I'm having none of that.'

'Funny, but that's the exact same words you used when we seen Skete Laird with Michelle Chapman, primary seven, Glenbow Primary. You were just like that back then. Anything you weren't involved in, you dismissed it. Anything to do with lassies and you ran a mile. You were the guy that dogged it on the last day when we had dances at the school, that was you. Scared.'

'Fuck, everybody did that.'

'Nah,' said Eddie, shaking his head, 'only thee, me and Fat Frazer.'

Dunx turned his head away. 'The act, the act is still sordid. You saying that if I go out and suck the Pope's cock everything'll be all right?'

'No,' said Eddie, 'don't be stupid. I just want you to remember how you were back then, and how you are about a lot of things still, a lot of other things. It's just something different, and what I want to know is what fucking difference does it make to you or anybody, anyway? It's as daft as saying folk in Belgium shouldn't be allowed to eat chocolate biscuits. I mean how much do you know about life that you can turn round to me and say what is and isn't wrong? I mean we're all going to fucking die, right, I'm not hurting anybody, in fact I'm making somebody very happy. There's two of us that are very happy. There's . . .'

'It's sordid! I hate that whole fucking scene, man. It's all just so casual. I hate all this 200 partners a year carry-on, I hate all that. How in the world are you supposed to develop a relationship living like that?'

'We're not all like that.'

'I thought you just said you had to go for tests.'

'That was a one-off, you go for tests even after a one-off. And, anyway, you're not exactly a symbol of fidelity yourself mind.'

'That's different, that's a macho thing. And I don't go to public toilets and stand there with my cock hanging out for 40 minutes hoping somebody'll notice me.'

'Neither do I,' said Eddie, 'and then again I don't think it's any of your business if folk want to do that. And Dunx,' Eddie eyeballed Dunx, 'I don't just go with anybody for the sake of shooting off my load.'

'Shite. That's a pity that.'

Everybody looked up. It was Wor Patrick that had spoken.

'Hey, sunshine,' said Wor Stevie, grabbing Wor Patrick by the hand. 'Shut it. You're spoken for remember.'

I was brian souter's rent boy!

ELLEN GALFORD

This piece was written for a live performance to launch Amnesty's LGBT campaign group in Scotland at the Edinburgh Radical Book Fair in May 2000, at the height of the homophobic 'Keep the Clause' campaign funded by Brian Souter.

I was Brian Souter's rent-boy!

Yes! Screaming out, in ten-foot letters, from all the tabloid front pages. I can picture those headlines now . . .

Especially while standing here on a rain-swept roadside in deepest Fife, in a village formerly famous for slaughtering witches. I am waiting for a Stagecoach bus.

Its proprietor, Mr Brian Souter, apparently considers me, my beloved partner of 21 years, and millions like us, all somewhat less than fully human. He has spent a fortune – enough, it's said, to equip several new operating theatres for the NHS – in his campaign to enshrine that prejudice in law. Nevertheless, he expects me to pay full fare from here to Kirkcaldy.

What's he so afraid of? Doth the lady protest too much? You don't have to be Dr Freud to wonder . . .

I briefly contemplate the delicious possibility that under the façade of that douce, righteous Dr Jekyll there lurks a lust-crazed, polymorphous, Judy Garland-loving Dr Hyde.

But a bigot's mind isn't a pleasant place to linger. Too much barbed wire and a whiff of Zyklon B. So my thoughts turn again to tasty little scenarios of sudden exposure.

'Bus Mogul's Ex-Love Stud Tells All!'

I run through the inventory of all my gay male friends, brothers-in-unnatural-deviance-and-depravity, and wonder which one I could persuade to set up a little honey trap. Strictly for the sake of the Struggle.

But their taste in men is far too good . . . not even in their wildest dreams . . . or mine. No volunteers.

No bus yet either. Unlike Mussolini's trains, Mr Souter's vehicles don't always run on time.

Then I suddenly remember another long-ago bus ride I took in Glasgow way back in the '70s, around the time I first came out as a lesbian. I was, in the style of that vanished era, wearing denim from head (blue Chinese worker's cap with a red Mao Tse Tung button on the forehead) to ankle. My jacket held enough badges to form the manifestos for Scotland's entire gamut of left-wing splinter groups (oh, we had millions of them, all hating each other even more than they hated the government of the day).

And somewhere in between Nuclear Power No Thanks (in English, French and Gaelic) and It's Scotland's Oil, was a large red and white badge that shouted in very big bright capital letters: Lesbians Ignite.

Anyway, I got on the bus and I paid my fare (the correct amount to get where I was going, because in spite of my loathing of the entire military-industrial complex, I was a very law-abiding little enemy of the capitalist state).

What I did not do was to take any notice of the driver. But I guess he took notice of me. Half a minute later he banged on the brakes and came pounding up the aisle. I'd slipped into a little romantic reverie and hadn't even noticed the sudden stop. But then I heard heavy breathing that was definitely not my own. I looked up to find a pair of nostrils flaring wider than the entrance to the Clyde Tunnel.

'See you! You're past your fare stage! Off the bus!'

Now, with a quarter century's worth of hindsight, I know I should have shown him my valid ticket, taken his number, and written in to report him. But having been so rudely ripped out of a very private movie scripted by Sappho and scored by Joan Armatrading, my reflexes were a little fuzzy.

And besides, even if that jacket full of political threats and slogans talked the talk, the person wearing it wasn't quite ready to walk the walk. So I just put up a few faint words of protest and went.

Only afterwards did it strike me that it must have been something to do with those badges.

Was it the Lesbians Ignite badge that upset him? Maybe he was mortified by having a daughter who wore motorcycle leathers and drank pints out of a straight-up glass. Or a wife who'd just left him for the woman next door. You never know.

Or was it the pink triangle harking back to concentration camps, or the one that said Glad To Be Gay? Or the more inclusive, more insinuating little purple and black number that demanded 'How dare you presume I'm heterosexual!'?

Anyway something (and it wasn't just a passenger wanting off) had really rung that bus driver's bell. But life went on and I soon forgot all about it.

Then, very recently, I spotted a little item in the inspiring rags-to-riches CV of Scotland's favourite new witch burner, Mr Souter. It said that, before God had rewarded him for his virtues by letting him gobble up most of the competition, our plucky hero had served time as a humble bus driver.

So now I wonder – as one does in this celebrity worshipping age – if, on that Glasgow bus long ago, I'd had a little brush with Someone Famous.

And it is my fondest daydream that somewhere out there lurks our aforementioned naughty little rent-boy. Maybe he too nurses the memory of a very different kind of encounter.

And if he does how I wish he'd come riding along this very road right now, as loud and gorgeous and flamboyant as Priscilla, Queen of the Desert. But, just like the Stagecoach X27, I hope he gets here soon. I wouldn't want him to miss the bus.

cain's book

ALEXANDER TROCCHI

ALEXANDER TROCCHI

I walked up Seventh Avenue and turned west on 23rd Street and made directly for the river. The bars were still open so the streets weren't deserted. On 23rd a police car trailed me for a few seconds and then glided past. Without turning my head I caught a glimpse of the man beside the driver, his head turned my way. I wasn't carrying anything that night.

I kept walking past Eighth, Ninth, and I walked up Ninth and turned left a few blocks later. I was walking slowly. Suddenly I was opposite an alley and in the alley about twenty yards away was the dark figure of a man standing close to a wall. He was alone under a small light near a garage door and he was exposing himself to a brick wall.

In terms of literal truth my curiosity was pointless. A man goes to a lane to urinate, an everyday happening which concerns only himself and those who are paid to prevent public nuisance. It concerned me only because I was there and doing nothing in particular as was quite ordinary for me, like a piece of sensitive photographic paper, waiting passively to feel the shock of impression. And then I was quivering like a leaf, more precisely like a mute hunk of appetitional plasm, a kind of sponge in which the business of being excited was going on, run through by a series of external stimuli; the lane, the man, the pale light, the flash of silver – at the ecstatic edge of something to be known.

The flash of silver comes from earlier; it was a long time ago in my own country and I saw a man come out of an alley. He had large hands. The thought of his white front with its triangle of coarse short hair came to me. I thought of the mane of a wolf, of the white Huns, perhaps because he stooped. Or perhaps because my own ears were pricked back and alert. In his other hand was the glint of something silver. As he walked past me he put his hands in his pockets. I looked after him. I realised I hadn't seen his face. Before I reached the corner he had turned into an adjacent street. I reached the intersection and he was entering a public house. I didn't see him in the bar nor in any of the side rooms. The bar was crowded with workmen, the same caps, the same white scarves, the same boots. He was not in the men's toilet.

Sitting there – an afterthought – I noticed that someone had cut a woman's torso deep in the wood of the door. As big as a fat sardine. There was no toilet paper. I used a folded sheet of the *Evening News*, part of which I tore carefully from the other part which was wet. It was water, and dust had collected. It had been jammed beneath the pipe under the cistern. The ink had run. I felt a necessity to read inside the wet pages. When I peeled them apart I found nothing of interest. A well-known stage actor was to be married. The paper was more than six weeks old. I remembered reading a few days before that he had since died. I couldn't remember whether he left a widow.

I drank one small whisky at the bar and left. The original impulse to find him had left me. The street was deserted, and the lane. On my way home I wondered why I had followed him. I wasn't after facts, information. I didn't delude myself from the moment I became aware of his shadow, although in self-defence I may have pretended to wonder, to seek safety in the problematic. I can see now I must have known even then it was an *act* of curiosity. Even now I'm the victim of my own behavior: each remembered fact of the congeries of facts out of which in my more or less continuous way I construct this document is an *act of remembrance*, a selected fiction, and I am the agent also of what is unremembered, rejected; thus I must pause, overlook, focus on my effective posture. My curiosity was a making of significance. I experienced a sly female lust to be impregnated by, beyond words and in a mystical way to confound myself with, not the man necessarily, though that was part of the possibility, but the secrecy of his gesture.

He wore the clothes of a workman, a cap, a shapeless jacket, and trousers baggy at the knees. He might have been a dustman, or a coalman, or unemployed. The hissing gas lamp cast his shadow diagonally across the lane and like a finger into the tunnel. As I came abreast of it I glanced through into the lane and when I saw him I caught my breath. The valve slid open. The faint lust at my belly made me conscious of the cold of the rest of my body. I felt the cool night wind on my face as I sensed my hesitation. It was the way he stood, swaying slightly and half-hidden, and it was then that I thought of his crotch, and of the stench of goats in the clear night air of the Tartar steppes, of the hairs of his belly, and of the stream of yellow urine from his blunt prick running in a broad, steaming sheet down the stone wall, its precision geometrical, melting the snow near the toes of his big boots. If I had had the nerve I might have approached him then and there instead of following him to the bar, but there was no kinetic quality in my hesitation. It lay on me like an impotence, cloying, turning my feet to lead. It was my cowardice which shattered me. The other knowledge, of the desire, came as no shock. Still, and with a sense of bathos, I found myself moving in pursuit of him when he lurched backwards into full view and passed me at the end of the tunnel where I stood. Did I invent the glint of silver? Endow him with a non-existent razor. The honing of the blade. When I couldn't find him in the bar, and after I had applied my skill to the torso on the wooden door, I returned to the lane and walked through the tunnel towards light. The singing gas lamp evoked memories of sensation, but faintly, and there was no element of anticipation. In the lane I looked over the wall at the windows of the dark tenements above. A pale light showed here and there from behind curtains. Above the level of the roofs the sky was darkening indigo and shifty with thin cloud. I thought: on such a night as this werewolves are abroad and the ambulances run riot in the streets. I kicked at the snow on the cobbles. My feet were cold. I walked home with a sense of failure, too familiar even then to shrug off easily. And then, when I entered the flat there was Moira wearing her drop earrings, waiting, hoping, at the portal of her day's thoughts, and I walked past her surlily, with no greeting.

Moira was sitting opposite me. This was before our divorce and before either of us came to America. I had put the incident of the man in the lane out of my mind. It was nearly ten o'clock. Two hours until New Year. One day followed another. Relief at having attained the limit of the old year made me uneasy. It wasn't as though I were walking out of prison.

Moira was hurt at my isolation. I could sense the crude emotion run through her. It was abrasive. She said I was selfish, that it showed in my attitude, on that of all nights. I knew what she meant.

She felt the need to affirm something and in some way or other she associated the possibility with the passing of the old year. 'Thank God this year's nearly over!' she said.

That struck me as stupid so I didn't answer.

'Do you hear what I say?' she demanded.

I looked at her speculatively.

'Well?' she said.

She began to speak again but this time she broke off in the middle. And then she walked across the room and poured herself a drink. She moved from one event to another without ever coming to a decision. It was as though she were trapped outside her own experience, afraid to go in. I don't know what it was she was going to say. She poured herself a drink instead. I watched her from where I was sitting. Her thighs under the soft donkey brown wool were attractive. She has still got good thighs. Her flesh is still firm and smooth to the touch; belly, buttocks, and thighs. The emotion was there, all the muscle and fibre. And then she was opposite me again, sipping distastefully at her drink, avoiding my gaze. She was trying to give the impression that she was no longer aware of me and at the same time she sensed the absurdity of her position. That made her uncomfortable. For her the absurd was something to shun. She had a hard time of it, retreating like a Roman before Goths and Vandals.

It occurred to me that I might take her. She didn't suspect. She didn't realise her belly was more provocative when it had been run through with hatred. Hatred contracts; it knitted her thicknesses. She was hotter then, only then. As she began to doubt my love she became a martyr and unlovable. But anger sometimes freed her; her muscles had experienced excitement . . . To walk across to her. She would pull herself up defensively and refuse to look at me. But her distance was unconvincing. She was not inviolable. That was the moment when I had to be in control of myself, for my lust tended to become acid in my mouth. I preferred her anger to her stupidity. It was something against which I could pit my lust. When I was confronted by her stupidity there took place in me a kind of dissociation, like the progressive separation in milk as it turns sour. I was no longer, as it were, intact, and she was no longer interesting.

I thought of the man in the lane. I had suddenly felt very close to myself, as though I were on the edge of a discovery. I was perplexed when I couldn't find him in the bar. I supposed he must have left while I was in the lavatory. The torso was cut deep in the wood, an oak leaf of varnish left where the pubic hairs were. I touched it with my forefinger, scratching varnish off with my fingernail. It struck me that it was too big. My wife had a big cunt with a lot of pubic hair, but not as big as that. It was heavily packed into her crotch. When I thought of it I always thought of it wet, the hairs close at the chalk white skin of her lower belly and embedded like filings in the pores.

from **cain's book** **189**

That made me think of her mother. I don't know why. The torso held my attention. I ran my fingers over it. The pads of my fingers were excited by the rough wood. I felt a slight prickling at the hairs at the back of my neck. I hadn't known wood so intimately before. I participated. I leaned against it. It felt good. That was when I first thought of my wife that night, more particularly, of the elaborate 'V' of her sex, standing with my thighs close to the door, touching. I took one drink and left. There was no sign of any man. I looked up and down the street. I felt it was going to snow.

My memory of that New Year's Eve joins those two together, my ex-wife Moira, at her most abject, and the Glasgow proletarian my mother feared, and whose image in the lane under the gaslight, with a thing of silver in one hard hand, elides mysteriously into myself. I often thought it must have been a razor, Occam's perhaps.

It occurred to me she was wearing those new earrings her cousin brought her from Spain. That was the second time I noticed the earrings that night. She had had her ears pierced a month before. The doctor did it for her. She said she thought drop earrings suited her.

It was New Year's Eve. Moira felt she was about to step across a threshold. The earrings represented her decision to do so. The date was marked on a calendar. I had wondered why she was wearing them. She had said earlier she didn't want to go to a cinema. Actually I had forgotten the date. I was surprised she was wearing earrings when I got back to the flat.

She was standing in the middle of the room, facing me. I felt she was waiting for me to say something. I had just come in. I was to notice the earrings. When I had done so we were to step hand in hand into a new calendar year. But I didn't notice them. I was still thinking of the man in the lane. And Moira herself got in the way, standing in the middle of the room, looking stupid, like she did in public when she thought no one was paying attention to her. Her eyes, as they say, expressed polite interest, indefatigably. At nothing, nothing. At the beginning I didn't see it. Perhaps it didn't exist at the beginning. I don't know. Anyway, it came to be as obtrusive as her mother's respectability. It had a murderous emphasis. As I say, I didn't see it at the beginning. I even looked the other way. But gradually it became clear to me that she was, among other things, stupid. A stupid bitch. And she had become a boring lay, unimaginative, like a gramophone. And so I didn't notice the earrings and my foot was not poised with hers on any threshold and my attention wandered.

I felt she was growing impatient, sitting there, nursing her drink, that she was not sure whether to make a scene, maintain her brittle composure there in the room, or go out quietly. The last move alone would have been authentic . . . or if she had offered me a drink . . . but she was incapable of making it. I think she thought she gave the impression of being dangerous. But Moira was never dangerous, or certainly wasn't at the time. She was not in the least improbable. When the clock struck 12 I heard chairs scraping across the floor of the flat above and the muffled noise of a woman's laughter. When my wife heard it . . . our chimes clock now continued its monotonous tick . . . she stiffened, and at that instant I caught her eye. I had seldom seen her so angry. She lunged out with her foot and kicked over the table. The whisky bottle splintered on the hearth and the whisky seeped out underneath the fender onto the carpet where it made a dark stain. For a moment, contemplating it and then me, she tottered like a skittle, and then, bursting into tears, she threw herself out of the room. She had removed her body with her anger. I felt suddenly quite empty.

My mind returned to the lavatory. I had examined the oak leaf and with my penknife I hewed it down to its proper size. It was no bigger than a pea when I had finished, a minute isosceles triangle with a rough bottom edge to it. I was pleased with the result. Leaning forward then on the handle of my knife, I caused the small blade to sink deeply into the wood at a low centre in the triangle. The knife came away with a small tug. The score, because of the camber of the blade, was most life-like; wedge-shaped, deep. I completed my toilet and returned to the bar. I drank a whisky. When I left I made straight for the alley.

The flats above formed a tunnel over it where it met the street so that one looked through darkness towards light. Just beyond the darkness, half out of sight round a jutting cornerstone, the man should have stood. I walked along the centre of the lane through the tunnel. The lane, a dead-end, was deserted. The dustbins were already out. I lingered a while. Perhaps I was the stranger you watched apprehensively from your kitchen window. When I left the lane it was already dark and a lamplighter was coming in my direction with his long lighted pole.

The flash of silver . . . the sudden excitement that was almost a nausea . . . the thought of Moira before we left Glasgow . . . the whole complex of the past: I relieved it all in that instant I caught sight of the man in the alley on my way back to the scow. The heroin had worn off but I was still pleasantly high from a joint that Tom and I had smoked on the way to Sheridan Square. The street was deserted. The man in the alley, facing the wall, hadn't noticed me yet. I was standing about ten yards from him. Like a man looking on a new continent. I felt the decision at my nostrils, and perhaps it was to communicate that to him, or perhaps it was simply to steady myself in my purpose – I lit a cigarette, cupping my hands over the match and holding them close to my face, causing the skin of my lower face to glow in the shaft of warmth from the match and leaving the skin about my lips tingling minutely in anticipation. The noise of the match striking and the sudden glow in the dark reached him. He froze momentarily and then looked sideways towards me. I could just make out the round yellowish face and the black moustache. There was a tightening pleasure at my entrails. I was quite sure of myself now. A nameless man. And something nameless had taken possession of me. I had simply to be and feel the workings of the nameless purpose in me, to grant, permissively to meet with, sensation unobstructed, rocked gently out of nightmare at him. He was buttoning up, slowly, it might have been reflectively, and then he turned towards me. There was something oblique and crablike in his movement. He was standing there, still under the electric lamp which shone on his shapeless double-breasted jacket at the shoulder and on the right side of his round face. I felt myself moving slowly towards him, a foot at a time, looking straight at his face. It seemed that he moved forward to meet me. In a few sensational seconds my front was close to his front and our faces were an inch apart. I felt the warmth of his ear against mine and his hand. Belt, thighs, knees, chest, cheek. A few minutes later we were walking very close together back to my scow at Pier 72.

I had been lying in the bunk for over an hour allowing thoughts of the past to mingle with my more immediate memory of the man's naked body pressing down on me. He had gone after about an hour, before dawn. I fell asleep almost at once.

He was Puerto Rican and he told me his name was Manuelo. He spoke almost no English and I almost no Spanish and it occurred to me as soon as we were in the cabin with one kerosene lamp lit and the dead silence broken only by the regular leak of water at the bilges of the scow . . . on us and infesting us with its own secrecy . . . it occurred to me that it was better that way. There were no common memories between us; we shared our male sex only, our humanity, and our lust.

It was not the first time I had had sexual experience with a man, but it was the first time it was not in one way or another abortive, it was the first time I had encountered a man who knew how to take all that was given without a trace either of embarrassment or of that shrill crustacean humour dedicated homosexuals sometimes adopt, and my body afterwards was heavy with the kind of satisfaction I had often envied women. He drank a cup of coffee before he left, his lips smiling and his teeth very white under his small black moustache. 'We see again? *Si*?' he said quietly. I nodded and placed my hand gently on his. '*Espero, Manuelo*,' I said. He left shortly afterwards. And I went at once to bed to savour the intense satisfaction at my limbs.

I woke with all the sexual memories of my past, allowing them to come and go, comparing them, the reliefs, the triumphs, the shames. Occasionally I felt an edge of self-justification in my thoughts, a plea too intense, an enthusiasm caught up and too lugubriously rationalised, but I was fundamentally very calm and still profoundly satisfied, physically with the mute certainty of my body, intellectually because I had broken through another limit and found that I could love a man with the same sure passion that moved me to women generally. The river noises of the morning began to come to me where I lay smoking a cigarette.

I don't know what it was that first attracted me to Tom unless it was that I felt him to be attracted to me. We just met, scored, and passed a few days together turning on. Most of my friends, especially those who don't use heroin, disliked him from the beginning, and I have often found myself rushing emotionally and intellectually to his defence. At times, after we had fixed and blown some pot, with a sleek thrust of my own soul, a thrust of empathy, I used to find myself identifying with him. I seldom do it now because Tom bores me nowadays, but I did so, often. But gradually I came to realise that he didn't think like I did, that he took my rationalisations too seriously or not seriously enough.

For example, he still talks about kicking, and at the same time he denies that he is hooked, and yet he has agreed with me again and again that if you simply put heroin down you are avoiding the issue. It isn't the horse, for all the melodramatic talk about withdrawal symptoms. It is the pale rider.

When Tom says: 'I'm gonna kick,' I say: 'Bullshit.' He becomes hurt and sullen. He feels I am deserting him. And I suppose I am.

He says he kicked before, the time he went to Lexington.

'Sure, and when you got back here you went straight up to Harlem and copped. A man doesn't kick, Tom. When he thinks in terms of kicking he's hooked. There are degrees of addiction, and the physical part has nothing to do with it. The physical bit comes soon and I suppose that then technically you're hooked. But with the right drugs you can kick that in a few days. The degrees of addiction that matter are psychological, like intellectually how long have you been a vegetable? Are you riding the horse or what? The trouble with you, Tom, is that you really put shit down. You use it most of the time, you dig it, but all the time you're putting it down, talking about kicking. It's not the shit that's got you hooked. You shelve the problem when you think in those terms. You talk all the time about copping and kicking. Talk about copping. Don't talk about kicking. Get high and relax. There are doctors, painters, lawyers on dope, and they can still function. The American people are on alcohol, and that's much more deadly. An alcoholic can't function. You've got to get up off your ass and stop believing their propaganda, Tom. It's too much when the junkies themselves believe it. They tell you it's the shit and most of the ignorant bastards believe it themselves. It's a nice tangible cause for juvenile delinquency. And it lets most people out because they're alcoholics. There's an available pool of wasted-looking bastards to stand trial as the corrupters of their children. It provides the police with something to do, and as junkies and potheads are relatively easy to apprehend because they have to take so many chances to get hold of their drugs, a heroic police can make spectacular arrests, lawyers can do a brisk business, judges can make speeches, the big pedlars can make a fortune, the tabloids can sell millions of copies. John Citizen can sit back feeling exonerated and watch evil get its deserts. That's the junk scene, man. Everyone gets something out of it except the junkie. If he's lucky he can creep round the corner and get a fix. But it wasn't the junk that made him creep. You've got to sing that from the rooftops!'

I have talked to him for hours. But in the end he always comes back to saying he's going to kick. That's because he hasn't really got much choice. He has no money. To get money he has to kick and there's a fat chance of his kicking without money. Still, it bugs me when he goes on talking about kicking.

'I'm gonna kick.'

'Man, you'll never kick.' Sometimes I don't even say it.

'You bastard, I will.'

'Okay, then, you'll kick.'

'Sure I will. You think I can go on like this?'

'You did before.'

'That's different. I was hung up then. I'll get the place fixed up good. You help me, Joe. If we only had some bread.'

'How much rent do you owe?'

'Not much, a few months.'

'How many months?'

'Must be about eight.'

'You've been goofing for eight months? You owe $320 back rent.'

'I'm gonna see him and say I'll pay it off, 20 a week.'

'Where are you going to get 20 a week?'

'I can get a job. I'll start kicking tomorrow. I can kick it in three days. I haven't got a real habit. I'll get dollies. I know a stud who knows where to get them cheap. I'll stay off shit. I won't touch the damn stuff.'

'Don't talk like an alcoholic.'

But it's like telling a man inflicted with infantile paralysis to run a hundred yards. Without the stuff Tom's face takes on a strained expression; as the effect of the last fix wears off all grace dies within him. He becomes a dead thing. For him, ordinary consciousness is like a slow desert at the centre of his being; his emptiness is suffocating. He tries to drink, to think of women, to remain interested, but his expression becomes shifty. The one vital coil in him is the bitter knowledge that he can choose to fix again. I have watched him. At the beginning he's over-confident. He laughs too much. But soon he falls silent and hovers restlessly at the edge of a conversation, as though he were waiting for the void of the drugless present to be miraculously filled. (*What would you do all day if you didn't have to look for a fix?*) He is like a child dying of boredom, waiting for promised relief, until his expression becomes sullen. Then, when his face takes on a disdainful expression, I know he has decided to go and look for a fix.

'You going to split, Tom?'

'Yeah, you comin'?'

I have gone with him sometimes.

'Look, you've still got some dollies, Tom.'

'I finished them.'

'Christ, already? Okay. I've got some goofballs and we can get a bottle of cough syrup. You can drink that.'

'That stuff's no good.'

'It'll cool you.'

Two o'clock in the morning. Sitting in Jim Moore's drinking coffee slowly. A few haggard men. A drunk woman trying to get someone to go home with her.

'I'm going home, Tom.'

'Where?'

'Bank Street. I'm going to try and get some sleep.'

'Look, let me come with you. If I stay around here I'll meet someone and get turned on.'

'I thought that's what we were sitting here for.'

'No, Joe, it'll be okay tomorrow. It'll be three days.'

'Okay. Come on, then.'

We get into the narrow bed and turn off the light. We lie awake for a while in the dark. I say: 'Look, Tom, you'll be okay.'

'I think I can sleep.'

I feel his arm move round me. I am suddenly very glad he is there.

I used to wonder if we would make love. Sometimes I felt we were on the brink of it. I think it occurred to both of us during those nights Tom slept with me in my single bed on Bank Street, his long brown arm round my body. There hasn't been much of what is ordinarily understood as sexuality in our relationship. The effect of heroin is to remove all physical urgency from the thought of sex. But on those nights we hadn't taken any heroin. We had drunk, turned on pot, taken whatever pills were available, and there were moments when our naked flesh touched and we were at the edge of some kind of release. If either of us had moved the other would probably have followed.

from **cain's book** **197**

MARTIN FOREMAN

MARTIN FOREMAN

ten million years

I have known and loved you for years, for centuries, for millennia. I have known and loved you since before knowledge and love, since before sight, before sound, before touch, before memory. I have known and loved you with every cell that has ever birthed and died in my body. I have known and loved you since you were me and we were one.

I first remember you as one among many who lazed in the shade of a thousand broad leaves or scampered from tree to tree in search of food, shelter or amusement. You were on the periphery of my vision, as I must have been at the edge of yours, no more than another broad-shouldered young male, posturing aggression or lazing in the sun, slowly and carefully picking nits from his own or another's hair. To you, I was the same, identifiable only through one unwitting habit or another, scratching a buttock when bored, yelping when a young child tried to steal my food. Unmated, we hovered around the pack, wary of our peers and afraid of our elders, day after day, year after year, eating and drinking, excreting, copulating and waiting for a future that neither, none, of us could conceive.

At times we found ourselves confronting each other in anger or in play, and, when we did so, there would be the briefest of moments in which our eyes met and some incomprehensible message flashed between us, a message bearing promise of ineffable knowledge and pleasure, but a message so weak that it died at birth, suffocated by the overwhelming urge to prove ourselves, to strike and to dominate. At other times, in rare moments of silence and tranquillity, we were haunted by desires we could not identify, unrecognisable shadows in a fog of ignorance and inexperience. I would find myself watching you, your shoulders hunched, your eyes darting hither and thither, your hands worrying the thick peel of some fruit, and I would wonder who you were, why I was staring at you and what I wanted from you. And in the eye-blink it took me to leap up and scurry towards you, these thoughts, as vague as they were disturbing, would be swept aside by greed for the food you held and apprehension of the hostility with which you rose to confront me.

Generations lived and died, bodies lengthened and thickened, hair thinned, jaws receded and faces expressed deepening knowledge and emotions. Driven by curiosity, we left the safety and comfort of the known for a world whose brightness both invited and terrified. Infants clinging to mothers, youngsters playing nervously, adults emboldened by each other's cries, we stepped out into the vast emptiness of the plains. There, despite the protection of petulant parents and grudging cousins, pain and fear multiplied in the terrors that lurked around us, below the horizon, behind the hillock, beneath the water. Many died from the violence of teeth and claws or the surprise of floods and rockfalls; others faltered and fell from no cause that we would discern. When we could, we would stop to stare uncomprehending at their bodies lying still, would wail at their silent, blank faces, would cradle them in our arms, willing our warmth to keep them safe and comfortable until life returned.

Your presence became more familiar when we took stones and wood and trudged the land in search of meat. It was then that the lives of males, of men, untethered by the demands of infants and children, by breasts which hung heavily with milk and comfort, began to drift apart from the lives of women. Each day we set out, 5, 10 or 20 of us, weapons in hand to strike at whatever prey we could find, one moment bearers of death, the next fleeing from its grasp. Sometimes you were the leader, the one we instinctively followed as we ran in exhilaration or panic through the long grass, the one unafraid to strike the first blow, the one first to rip and devour the flesh. Sometimes I led, urgently gesturing the others to crouch behind the few rocks and trees that offered cover, one eye on our quarry, the other on whoever waited to take my place and my right to food and life. Sometimes we both held back, without the courage to lead, but always with the hunger that never left us in peace.

In the forest we had not needed to speak beyond the few cries that identified food and water, safety and danger. It was on the plains that words emerged, sounds that enabled us to identify and pursue our game and to enact the chase for our women and children. With each generation new sounds were born, for ourselves and for the animals which fed us, for the trees and caves that offered shelter, for the elements that protected and persecuted us, for feet pounding across the ground, for sharp stone cutting into gut, for the bloody infant emerging and the last breath sighing. And with each new sound that mirrored the world we could see and hear and touch, light was thrown upon other worlds, the worlds that lay deep in our sleep and far behind our closed eyes.

Seasons rushed by, bearing heat and cold, rain and drought, wind and calm. We hunted, moved and hunted again. We stumbled and sped across rocks, grass, sand, mud and marsh. We ripped sinew and bone from steaming carcases and gnawed at dried or rotting meat. We returned to our families in haste and at leisure, starving and satisfied, bearing food and sometimes our dead. I learnt to wait and watch for you, to seek out the angle and swiftness of your arm, the tension of your haunch, the light in your eyes. I began to welcome your sharp, strong smell and your deep rough voice. And at night, as the moon watched and the sky sparkled, I greeted the roughness of your skin and the matt of your hair as together we lay shivering under thin and sparse hides.

We had rutted all our lives, since the fire in our groins first flared and sought to spend itself. In earlier days we had rutted almost as frequently as we had breathed, from pleasure or from duty, clinging to friends and strangers alike in ritual motions that confirmed status and power. Like defecation, the rapid contraction of muscles was performed without thought. If you were my partner I welcomed your body's proximity, but never thought to extend it or to seek you out for that purpose. With time we began to recognise that copulation between male and female brought forth infants and with that knowledge our perception of ourselves and of others changed. We rutted less, sticks and stones expressing domination with greater force than proffered buttocks or groins, and mated more to beget children and symbolise new concepts of ownership and control.

But on those cold nights far from our women and children, exhausted, sometimes hungry, sometimes sated, our bodies shifting again and again to ease the stiffness and pain that seeped into our bones from the hard, uneven soil, the demanding rhythm of our hips, the urge to piss out our seed as we thoughtlessly pissed out our water, gave way to slower, gentler motion. We became aware of pleasure and of a desire to offer that pleasure to each other, we heard the echo of emotions we could neither identify nor comprehend. Tentatively, our hands reached out, uncertain whether to strike, pinion and control, or to hold, welcome and embrace. Sometimes the action of the one raised the wrath of the other and sometimes it was indifference that led to anger – but in those moments in which our bodies rocked in harmony, our mouths trembled and our eyes questioned, we were held by a force as powerful and uncontrollable as the driving rain or burning sun.

Years passed. We changed and were no different. We knew each other and were strangers. At times grey streaked your hair and beard and the pelt around your waist hung tattered and stiff; at times you were a naked youth on his first kill, bolder and more vulnerable than his brothers and cousins; at times you loped ahead with a man's pride and grace, trophies dangling from your waist or their image tattooed to your face and breast. I saw you left behind with the women, maimed or misshapen and unable to hunt; I watched you run from my agony and wounds; I saw your body abandoned in the dust. Your thin form leapt at me, one of 20 or a hundred desperate for food; you stood uncertain amongst the bloated forms of those from whom we stole. Each blow that I struck at such moments of enmity, each wound that severed muscle and spurted blood, was driven by a hatred and anger that only now do I recognise was directed at myself, with some pain and incomprehension that you, time and again, must have slashed, battered and destroyed my tired, aching body.

We moved north to the land of cold, where our words hung white in the air before us. We wore thick hides that stank of the beasts we had killed, and through the deep snow chased the lumbering mammoths, great beasts with sad eyes, that kept us alive. There were many good years when at night we huddled together and I felt your body and its warmth and hardness. We talked for the pleasure of speech itself, to relive the hunt, to praise or blame our companions, to describe wounds we had received or escaped, to pray to the gods, seen and unseen, whom we had begun to worship. We still had no words for our longings, few concepts beyond dissatisfaction in our existence and rare contentment in each other's presence, but in our silences we offered each other peace. And even without words I knew that, no matter how similar the action, if my sex hardened and my seed pumped onto your belly or between your legs, if your warmth spilt onto my hand or into my bowels, the body I held was yours and not my mate's and my desire for you was deeper and more powerful than I had ever known for any woman.

Fire, clothing and permanent shelter allowed us to settle. In some places we did, in others we continued to hunt and wander. Women watched the seasons and the soil, saw seeds spring into shoots, learned to plant and to hoard. With these skills estrangement deepened, as the balance between the sexes, between feeder and fed, protector and protected, tipped further askew. Resentment and anger grew and more and more frequently the strength that we used against our prey and our enemies turned against our women, against each other.

Still you and I lived apart, our daily lives dominated by the communities in which we lived, by the unforgiving web of deference and loyalties each of us owed and were owed. As infants we clung to our mothers, as children we feared our fathers, as young men we were rivals for the mate who would keep our fire, bear our children and grow our crops. As adults, even as we enjoyed a few years of strength and laughter before accident, war or invisible disease struck us down, we were preoccupied with our women and children, with the hunger that was seldom more than a day away, with enemies both real and imagined.

Sometimes we found each other as adolescents, in that year when, too old for our mothers and too young for our fathers, we were free to go where we wished and play as we willed. Then we might become aware of each other's presence and find ourselves in rare privacy hesitating to express frightening new emotions in words, gestures or caresses. All too often we were swept apart by the demands of adulthood, yet, as there had been on the plains, there were times when we could hunt and walk together, eat and sleep side by side, share the warmth of our bodies and the heat of our desire. Then, years later, alone in age, I might huddle, hunch-backed, under a blanket of leather or wool and, as I stared into the fire or the shadows of trees on a moonless night, remember an hour, a night, a day spent in your company, a day that I held as dear as a lifetime with the mother of my children and with children who ignored me as I ignored my father before them.

Once, perhaps, in a hundred years, we might have time with each other, if our wives had died, if no other women needed husbands and if our children had returned to the kinship of their mothers' families. Forced by custom to maintain households empty of other bodies, other voices and smells, we lived solitary lives, pitied by our tribe, rejected if we had not proved our worth in battle, the hunt or wisdom. But it was in those dying years, with no more to distract us than the source of our next meal, that you and I had the freedom to spend time with each other, to search for pleasures that our minds, if not our bodies, could share. Those were golden years indeed, when stiff bones rested against old trees and quiet voices shared memories and dreams.

Even more rarely, as young men the urge to be together would be so strong that we refused to take wives, insisting instead that we live together and share each night a bed. Some tribes expelled us, forcing us into the wilderness and a daily struggle for life; others accepted us, grudgingly or in wonder, the objects of suspicion and ridicule or of respect and goodwill. But whatever our fate, I accepted it if I shared it with you, for then as now, in ways that I have never understood, your presence was all that I needed to dull every pain of the body and mind.

Tens, hundreds, thousands of years passed. Our communities spread across the globe in search of food, warmth and distance from our enemies. Civilisations grew and shrivelled, arts flourished and died, beliefs multiplied, as we danced on warm sandy shores, carved homes out of rock, tempted mammal and fish from the waters of icy oceans. Our features also changed, but whether your eyes were narrow and your belly hairless, or your lips full and your skin dark, whether your eyes faded to blue and your hair to yellow, whether you were short and plump or tall and skeletal, you never failed to attract me, the hardness in my groin ever seeking the hardness in yours as magnets seek the pole. Yet as much as I desired your body, it was always more than I needed. I would be drawn by the valour that had killed a lion and cowed a village, moved by the laughter you gave your children, swayed by the wisdom that ruled a village or a kingdom.

With knowledge came wealth and with wealth came leisure for the few and poverty and despair for the many. Sometimes we shared riches, sometimes we shared destitution and sometimes destitution and riches formed a bridge across which one stretched a hand to the other. We were more adept now at recognising our attraction for each other, at recognising that we were not alone, yet still we were far from always admitting our longing. Sometimes the men amongst whom we lived and the gods whom we honoured and feared forbade us from expressing our dearest wish, to be together. At other times our desire might be acknowledged and celebrated by others as well as ourselves. Thus as a boy I was wooed by you, as soldiers we fought together, as priests we worshipped together. Over the years legends would grow up about us, a kernel of truth becomes a tree of fiction, the emperor with the cut sleeve, the homely philosopher and his handsome pupil, and, again and again, the warrior who died with his companion or who sought to bring his companion back from death.

Yet even when our affection was commended, we were seldom admired as lovers seeking equals. We were accepted only if our need for each other was sanctioned by pedagogy, religion or war. I might teach you to be a man, you might instruct me as a warrior, one or other would don sacred robes and tread the awesome path of the gods. But if we were both of a similar background and age and wished no more than to lead quiet lives together alongside our neighbours, seldom were we accepted. For hundreds of generations the emotions that could be happily flaunted if one was fourteen and the other three times his age had to be hidden if we were both in our twenties or thirties. Strange, is it not, that within little more than a lifetime the opposite has become true.

For these reasons and others, for each time that we found each other, many more times we failed. We did not recognise the one we sought or did not even know that we searched. Our desire would be stunted, still-born, no more than the joyless friction of two strangers in a deserted field or the banter of hothouse intellects. Our deepest needs denied, we might explode into violence, to leave a stranger raped, a wife beaten, a slave killed. In youth and middle age we revelled in others' weaknesses and in old age loss and impotence made us bitter and reviled. Afraid of each other and ourselves, I would abuse you or fall victim to your abuse, as we became in turn servants overworked and underpaid, children seduced into incomprehension and fear, adults betrayed by blackmail and exposure. Often your body was no more than one among hundreds, prizes I awarded myself for a contest I misunderstood; at times it offered not the challenge and reward of an equal but nothing more than the misplaced security of unfulfilled childhood, or the animal warmth we found beneath the stars millennia ago.

And through it all we lived in a world of wives and children, of neighbours and friends, wars and peace, politics and commerce. Often I resented, feared, bullied, robbed and killed the women who shared my life. But there have also been times when I have recognised the love – and it has been love, that most recent and complex of emotions – that they have borne me and I have loved them in return. For if the truth is told, as we grow old and more distant from those around us, it does not matter who we love if they love us with the same intensity. I have loved my children too, if not each one and at every moment. Sometimes it seemed that they were no more than pets or farm animals running about my feet, more expensive and less rewarding than a hunting dog or well-fed swine, but at other times their laughter and affection and vulnerability has knocked me from my height to their feet and drawn tears of joy and sorrow from my eyes.

But such emotion is fleeting in comparison to the love that has survived across generations, across countless lives, survived even when we did not know we loved. I have loved you without ever speaking to you, without you ever knowing of my existence. I have loved you as a cousin, as a teacher or a pupil, a minion or a rich man, a captive or a king. I have loved you as a stranger, as a familiar, as an enemy, a friend. I have loved your smile and laughter, your sorrow and pain, your dedication and insouciance. I have loved you because you were who you were, because you could do nothing ever but awaken love in me.

And that love remained and deepened even in the twilight, when each day we feared the cough, the fever, the lethargy that opened the door to the malady that strikes us again and again. Although we had seen each other die often and die young, from the wounds of war, from other illnesses, from murder or accident, and with each death we wept long bitter tears, I was overcome by the monotonous predictability of this new disease, by the vision of youth and health evaporating again and again like water on a sunny day. I raged too that it struck us now, when for the first time we can meet and live together openly as equals, as lovers, as partners. We are learning to defeat it, but too often it still defeats us.

Yet love remains. Even as my eyes grow dim and your voice fades, your presence becomes stronger, so that the hand which grasps me, the caress of my brow, your whisper in my ear, the faint smell of your sweat, your lips holding mine, all tell me what I have always known, always believed and always want to hear, that you love me, that you always have and always will, as I love you more and more with each dying breath.

In each death we are reborn. I see you everywhere, as you see me, in a myriad of lives and ages and communities. In some cities we kiss and flirt on the streets, we open businesses and elect politicians, effortless days flowing into effortless nights where we gather in bars and restaurants and private homes and celebrate our peace and our wealth and our love. But these opportunities are still rare; in many towns we can only meet in night-time parks, dark alleys and stinking urinals, our hands grasping, our bodies straining towards each other through the thick leather jackets or thin cotton robes, our goal no more than an orifice to enter, an itch to satisfy, an orgasm to expend. And even more often, whether we live in our richest or our poorest lands, even that brief human contact is but a dream that comes to us in the night and from which we waken angry, unhappy or afraid.

I do not know what the future brings. I only know that it will be many more generations before we earn the respect of all the communities in which we live, the respect which will allow us to love each other openly, permanently and unconditionally. But in my heart

I fear that moment will never come. It is not that we have enemies, although there are still many who hurt us as we sometimes hurt ourselves, but that we are all, every man, woman and child on this planet, destroying our home as quickly and as eagerly as we once created it. As we do so, we harm each other and leave those who follow to face a world as hostile as the one that you and I faced ten million years ago. But if that happens, if forests die, cities explode, seas overflow and only one thousand of us survive, I will not be afraid, because I know that you and I will still be here. And in that dim, uncertain future, as now, as always in our past, wherever I am, if I am with you, I am happy, and if I am alone, I search for you across a crowded or deserted world and hope and pray that you see me.

from

the house on rue st jacques

CHRISTOPHER WHYTE
CHRISTOPHER WHYTE

László was of mixed Hungarian and Polish descent, and went under many names in the House on Rue St Jacques. The Polish version was difficult to pronounce. Often he would present himself under the Italian form, Ladislao, which was the most musical and my favourite. At other times it was Antoine, and because several visitors used that name, you could have no idea till you set eyes on him exactly who had come. His body was smooth-skinned and almost hairless. His complexion was ruddy and he had a burning auburn head of hair, just like the leaves of horse chestnut trees in the grip of the first frosts, hanging like stark cries on branches which will shed them before long. The set of his eyes and his chin had an alien, Asiatic quality that set me dreaming. You have to remember I was only 20, and had not travelled at all, with the exception of one single, momentous train journey north to Paris from Oporto. I decided that his ancestors had worn that look when they galloped westward out of the steppes, and beheld the Carpathian mountains rising into the sky in front of them. Foolish romanticism. But it helped me at the time.

When I saw László in the House on Rue St Jacques, it was generally in the Chinese Room on the second floor. It got that name from the

Second Empire wallpaper, with its repeated pattern of scribes and musicians, whiling away the hours in gardens supplied with ponds, bridges and arcades that hung suspended above their pastimes with the sinuous languor of creeping plants. The two lamps on either side of the bed would catch the gold of the design and set it glinting, making the room resemble nothing more than an underwater cave, with deflected sunlight playing on the movements of the fishes. The curtains were green, also inlaid with gold. For reasons of discretion, and in order to dampen the noise of carriages and motors from the street below, it was normal practice to draw them, and to keep the window shutters tightly fastened. But sometimes when I was alone there, and more frequently with László, especially at twilight, my preferred time, or else long after midnight, I would open both cautiously, having first ensured the room was in darkness, and press my face to the window, so as to contemplate the city like an immense peepshow, just beyond the glass.

László was personal secretary to the manager of the Paris Opera, and continued in this position even after the German invasion. I saw his employer on two occasions, at festive banquets in the upper dining-room of the House on Rue St Jacques. He was a distinguished-looking gentleman in his late fifties, running to fat, with a grizzled beard and splendid whiskers, of a kind that had gone out of fashion shortly after the First World War. László said he was the spitting image of Saint-Saëns in the last photographs. He had been a close associate of the composer when much younger.

That was how László came by the marvellous story of Saint-Saëns' visit to Moscow. He insisted that the Frenchman, Tchaikovsky and Anton Rubenstein had locked themselves in a practice room through one long afternoon. Rubenstein's job was to play different ballet scores on the piano, while the two composers indulged in a peccadillo that entranced them both, imitating the principal ballerinas of the day. László claimed that the session had culminated in a pas de deux. He was uncertain who had danced the male part, who the female. The story gave me great delight, though I am too much of a sceptic to give it much credence. Saint-Saëns was a model of sobriety in his homeland. His gravity of demeanour was innate and cannot be attributed to the personal tragedies he suffered (the break up of his marriage and the loss of a son, who fell to his death from a window of their apartment). He must surely have limited such extravagant behaviour to select company on his professional trips and, who knows, to the repeated visits to Arab lands which were the cause of so much gossip.

László's affair with his employer had been passionate, at least in the early years. When I saw him, the older man was still handsome, so I do not find it difficult to believe that he was exceptionally fine looking even in his forties. Whether his visits to the House on Rue St Jacques were motivated primarily by the gastronomical delights on offer, or had reasons of a different, amorous nature, I am at a loss to say. He was aware of his secretary's fondness for the place and, according to László, knew who I was too, and something of my story. There was not the slightest trace of jealousy or even embarrassment in the looks he directed towards me across the table.

Things would have gone very differently in the first days of their relationship. I heard the tale I am about to tell on an evening I remember well, not long after Christmas. Snow had fallen heavily for two days and was lying on the city streets, so that the passage of carriages, motor cars and even pedestrians had a different, muted resonance. I cannot say whether lovemaking heightens one's sensitivity to noises or if it is simply that, after orgasm, in the course of which one's own body and the body one is entangled with can come to seem the centre of the world, silence takes on a special quality, so that all noise, from whatever source, is magnified. I remember pulling the bell and instructing Masnière, the major-domo, to have the fire stoked. László pulled the sheet up to the level of our chests but, from the glance of wonder and desire which the houseboy threw us, I realised we must look unusually beautiful together. Once he had completed his work, we skipped from the bed and curled up on the carpet in front of the fire, which was the only source of light in the room. The reflection of the flames played across László's torso. A different person might have been reminded of the flames of hell. I, however, thought of László as a winged creature who could fly through fire unharmed. The russet glow of his skin made it his natural element.

He had spent the latter years of the First World War in a secluded castle in Slovakia. I cannot recall the name of the place. The estate belonged to relatives of his father. László was sent there with his mother and his younger brother so that they could be far from the zone of conflict, and proceed with their education in tranquil surroundings. As he described it to me, it was a setting of enormous beauty. But the isolation and boredom he experienced were well-nigh unbearable. The peasants spoke a Slavic dialect. Communicating with them in his rudimentary German proved laborious in the extreme.

Melancholy prompted him to take longer and longer walks through the nearby hills. Once the lands around the castle held no more secrets he began exploring the neighbouring estate, although the boundary between the two was distant by one full hour's brisk walk. On his second visit, he was making his way through a lime grove when he heard strains of music coming from afar. They stopped, started, then stopped again.

Someone was playing the piano. The harmonies were rich, modernistic, experimental, and what he could make out of the music had a powerfully Oriental feel to it. Drawing near, he glimpsed a summer-house beneath the branches. Although it was still afternoon, candles burned inside, for the place was in shadow. The summer-house consisted of a single, enormous room. There was no road or even a path in sight. Nonetheless, it contained a full-size piano, looking as if it had grown there naturally from seed. A young man was bent over the keys, so absorbed in the act of composing he had no inkling of László's approach. The face, as he described it, had the shape of a heraldic shield, with a broad forehead and a slightly pinched chin. The musician had a moustache and long, straight hair, neatly cropped everywhere except on his forehead. One strand kept slipping down and getting into his eyes while he played. He would throw it back impatiently.

The contrast between the music he was producing, the intensity of his concentration and his irritation at the unruly strand was so comical László could not stop himself laughing. He could have sworn he made no sound. Nevertheless, the composer chose that precise moment to look up. An expression of horror swept across his face. László took to his heels, not pausing for breath till he was again within sight of the castle.

He was about 16 at the time. He said nothing to his mother or his brother about the strange discovery. He was not even sure that he would manage to find his way back to the place. In any case, he had decided that to disturb the man at his work again would be too great a violation of his privacy. During the night, he came to view the matter very differently. By the time dawn broke, he was impatient to return. He had a hunch the young composer might lie long in bed in the mornings, so there was no point in hunting for him before lunch. The meal stretched out interminably, given László's impatience to be on his way. All he could think of was the lime grove, with the hidden summer-house and its mysterious inhabitant.

The man was a Pole, as things turned out, whose family had lands in Volhynia, where the vast Ukrainian steppes begin. His name was Alexander and he had been cut off from all his relatives by the outbreak of the war. By the time László met him, the Bolsheviks had already seized power in St Petersburg. Alexander felt sure his family had fled, though he had no notion of their whereabouts. Most likely they had travelled to Odessa, then taken ship to a Bulgarian port or to Istanbul, before making their way overland, north to Warsaw. There had been two splendid grand pianos, he told László, in the parlour at the front of the family mansion, brought there at huge expense from Leipzig 20 years before. Rumour had it that the peasants, at the cost of great manoeuvring with ropes and levers, had got them out onto the lawn, then sunk them in the ornamental pond at the bottom of the garden. They haunted his dreams, swimming to and fro in ungainly fashion in the murky waters, still giving out strains of the music he had composed on them.

When László got there on the second day, no one was to be seen. It was easier than he expected to locate the place. He was gifted with a keen sense of direction. A light breeze blew. It was late spring and the leaves of the lime trees were pale green. They made him think of new clothes worn for the first time, which will never again look quite so fine. He could not banish the idea that his intrusion was making the trees restless. Finding the summer-house empty, he felt afraid. Nonetheless, he tried the door. It was open. There was a heap of densely scribbled pages on top of the piano. It fascinated him to think that the signs careering across them might be a transcription of the music he had heard the previous afternoon. He sat down and tried to pick out on the keys a piece by Bach, one he had studied when taking piano lessons in Kaschau in the years before the war.

The fragrance of a cigarette alerted him to Alexander's presence. László told me his host treated him with easy familiarity from the very start, as if they had been friends for a long time. They communicated in a mixture of French and Polish, though László stumbled in both languages, more from embarrassment and lack of practice than from faulty knowledge. He spoke Hungarian at home. The composer offered to play him the central section of the piece he was engaged on, which had been causing him considerable difficulty. Then he produced a volume of duets. When László hesitated, suggesting he ought to let the other man get down to work, Alexander laughed and told him not to worry. He had become obsessed with the piece, he said. It would do him good to have company and be distracted.

The day was brighter than the one before. They did not have to light the candles until dusk. Cautiously, László brought the conversation back to the music which had first drawn him to the place. The other man, not more than ten years his senior, was reticent at first. But after repeated questioning, he explained that it had been inspired by a journey.

The year before the war began, he travelled to Italy with a close associate, who was a novelist. Not content with exploring Tuscany and Umbria, they pushed further south past Naples and Rome to Palermo, arriving there at the start of November. Sicily, Alexander claimed, was his spiritual home. He loved its blend of contradictory cultures. The place was neither Christian nor Islamic but both. And beneath these recent strata one sensed an all-pervasive paganism. Was Eurpides' *The Bacchae* not set in Sicily? The ancient Greeks had established some of their most magnificent colonies there and in the heel of Italy. Had László heard of Sybaris, so famed for the refined lifestyle of its citizens that they became a byword for decadence and effeminacy?

The Polish man was warming to his theme. He and his novelist friend had travelled on to Tunis, visiting the ruins of Carthage and losing themselves in the meandering bazaars of the North African cities. With an odd, piercing glance he asked if László knew of André Gide's book about the seed which did not die, or was familiar with the work of Oscar Wilde, and seemed to be relieved when the younger man shook his head in response.

We are accustomed, he said, to view Christianity and Islam as cultures locked in conflict, enshrining opposed values and customs. As a consequence, the rich interchange occurring in places like Sicily had been either forgotten, or the memory of it deliberately suppressed. Did László realise how much the civilisation of medieval and Renaissance Spain owed to Islam, without mentioning the Jews? Did he realise that the image of Christ as the Good Shepherd was not Christian in origin at all, and that statuettes of a young god carrying a lost sheep upon his shoulders, dating from the time of the Ptolemies, had been dredged up from the waters of the Nile, and were now on display at the museum in Berlin? Where had the troubadours found the inspiration for their stanza forms, or for their cult of courtly love, if not in the minstrels of the Arab courts?

Alexander aimed to capture the magic of Sicily in the opera which he was writing. The plot had been worked out in collaboration with his novelist friend. The god Dionysus was to make an appearance at its climax. The composer's eyes lit up with mystical fervour at the mention of that magical name, and he puffed convulsively at his cigarette before going on. The first time the pagan god came onto the stage, he would be disguised as a wondrous youth, a shepherd brought before the ecclesiastical authorities to answer charges of leading the peasantry astray with his uncanny songs and sermons.

László remained impervious to all the hints contained in what he heard. He assured me they had not kissed each other so much as once through that long summer. The older man did not attempt to touch him. Yet I have no doubt theirs was a great love. Alexander dedicated poems to him in ill-scanning French, played over passage after passage of the nascent opera as it took shape, and even spoke of a novel he planned to write, one of whose principal pair of characters was to have embodied the features he most admired in his young friend.

One day early that autumn László found the summer-house locked. The piano was swaddled in blankets to protect it from the approaching cold. All the large glass windows, except for one, were hidden by shutters. Beneath a stone on the doorstep was an envelope containing a transcript of the poems, still in László's possession, and a short letter from Alexander. He had been unable to summon up enough courage to announce his imminent departure. His family were in Vienna. He had been called to join them at short notice.

László fell silent at this point. My dominant emotion, I must admit, was jealousy. Absurd, perhaps, since these events had taken place two decades before we met, and it was clear the story had no happy ending. The fire was dying down. Though the shutters and the curtains were closed, cold seeped into the room from the street outside, like an invisible effluent attaching itself to skin and furnishings. I got up to poke the fire, then took a bolster and a blanket from the bed so that we could make ourselves more comfortable.

He left many things unsaid. He was unable rather than unwilling to put them into words. Meeting the composer had been the first effective intimation that, throughout his life, he would be a lover of men and not of women. It culminated in a loss which had overwhelmed him, long before he could learn to give even the crudest expression to his wayward feelings. Alexander was a master of circuitous and inconclusive phrases. The two had coined no language for the bond that linked them. That, in my opinion, was the Polish man's real crime. He awakened something in his friend without offering him a name for it. Abandoned without any shadow of a warning, László had no way of expressing the grief he experienced. I myself loved László, after a fashion. I neither shrank away nor tried to comfort him. All I did was wait for the silence to end. At last he turned onto his side and drew me close, so that I was now able to see the whole of his face.

'I am going to tell you,' he began, and his voice had a croaking quality that alerted me to the intensity of his emotion, 'about one of the most awful moments in my life. I remember the date exactly. It was 24 September 1927. Guillaume and I' (Guillaume was the name of his lover and employer) 'went to lunch at Sauvigny's, to meet a composer he wanted to commission a ballet from. He mentioned that the man was Polish, had recently scored a moderate success in Prague with an opera set in Sicily, and was "one of the sisterhood". But I failed to make the connection with that summer during the war. He was bringing a concert pianist friend along, a married man with three children. Telling me this was Guillaume's way of warning me to avoid banter and indecent allusions. He was still jealous of me at that time. Informing me about the tastes of the people we mixed with and of what behaviour was appropriate was one way of asserting control over me. I am a flirt by nature, and was even more of one in my younger days. Innocent dalliance on my part had led to major scenes between us, with Guillaume threatening to end the relationship and avoid any further contact.

'Our guests were late. When they were ushered to our table, I lifted my head and my eyes met Alexander's. He looked infinitely older, drawn and haggard. His hair was streaked with grey. I could not have known, but he was already suffering from the illness which would kill him. Catching sight of me, he stopped in his tracks and grasped his friend's arm convulsively. The cigarette he was smoking dropped from his lips without him seeming to notice. Then his face went rigid. His whole body did, in fact, as he turned to greet Guillaume. We studiously avoided looking at one another even as they introduced us. The pianist friend had already guessed the only possible explanation for our behaviour. Both he and Alexander were aware of Guillaume's reputation for possessiveness. The married friend kept sending me pleading glances of complicity, while doing his best to keep up a conversation about a recent concert tour to Britain. Alexander needed money desperately. Any hint of unwelcome emotional entanglements would have put paid to his hopes of a contract. It turned out that Stravinsky was lunching at a nearby table. He joined us, relieving myself and Alexander of any need to talk.'

'What happened then?'

'We met twice more, in secret, at great risk. My first thought was that we should become lovers and do everything that had been left undone in the past. But it was out of the question. He was far too ill, for one thing. The second time we saw each other he coughed blood into a napkin. I kept it. I still have it. We sat for more than an hour both times, in dingy cafes on the outskirts of Paris, the sort of places neither Guillaume nor anyone else we knew would ever have set foot in. We could not find words. There were no words.'

If words were lacking, then perhaps there was music. I know now the full name of László's composer and I have heard his opera, not in a live performance, but broadcast on the radio. I have also listened to the songs he wrote during that marvellously productive summer of 1918, in a secluded summer-house in Slovakia, while Europe's ageing empires disintegrated around him, and his family made their way from port to port up the Dalmatian coast, till they reached Trieste and could get a train to complete the next leg of the journey north to Vienna.

The kind of jealousy László's story inspired in me was complex. Of course I envied the composer for the importance he had assumed, and still had, in László's life. More precisely, for the feelings he had been able to inspire, and which 20 years had done little to assuage. More than anything, I envied László's ability to experience that degree of loss, of tragedy. My life at that time had a monotonous quality, as if no one had the power to touch me deeply, or penetrate my defences. And it would continue to be so, until the day I met Rémy.

KEITH ADAMSON

KEITH ADAMSON

mother nature's son

The old barman regarded the stranger with suspicion as he set a vodka tonic down and wiped his nose on the sleeve of his cardigan. 'Who did you say you were looking for?'

'Donnie McKracken,' the young man said again, thinking he'd made himself perfectly clear the first time.

'Rab, there's a fellow here looking for Donald.' This was addressed to a red-faced farmer sitting alone in the far corner of the bar, smoking quietly at a pipe. He had an empty pint mug in front of him. 'Rab'll tell you.'

The young man went over to Rab's table. 'I'm looking for someone called Donnie McKracken. I've been to his house but it looks deserted. I was wondering if he still lives there.'

Rab looked at him without any kind of expression. 'You'd better sit down.'

'Can I get you a drink?'

'Same again. A pint of heavy.'

His glass recharged, Rab wet his lips and stared at the young man. 'Donald's dead,' he said.

He heard the information but couldn't assimilate it. Feeling his face flush, he took a large gulp of his drink. 'When?' he asked.

'Couple of months ago. Came to a sticky end in his car. He was a close one, that boy.'

'Oh, God.'

Rab watched him finish his drink with a kind of curiosity, as if trying to gauge from his reaction what business this stranger had with young Donald.

'I had hoped I might stay over with him. Now I suppose I'd better find a hotel. Is there one in the village?'

Rab shook his head. 'Nah, you'll need to go into town.'

He glanced at his watch. It was eight o'clock. He could use another drink. 'Would you like a whisky with that?'

Rab nodded.

The young man returned with fresh glasses and resumed his seat next to the farmer. He wanted to ask all about Donnie but hardly knew where to begin. When he looked up, he saw Rab staring at him over his raised glass.

'Oh, cheers,' he acknowledged. 'Did you know Donnie well?'

'Aye. He'd lost both his folks when he was quite small. He used to work in here. We were all a mite fond of him.' The whisky seemed to be loosening his tongue. 'He was not one for the lassies, you know. He tended to keep his own company, like. Some of the lads said at one time, when he passed 21 and still not married, maybe he was one of these queer folk you hear about; but I said, no, not our Donald. And he was nae as quiet as folks thought, either, once he'd had a dram or two in him.'

Eyes, making contact along the bar counter, glancing tentatively, but interested. What will he say if I offer to buy him a drink? He says, a whisky, please. He has a soft Highland lilt, which heightens his appeal, and when he smiles, dimples form at the ends of his mouth.

I ask him what brings him to Glasgow and he's embarrassed that I've sussed out his accent. He smiles again, with a mischievous glint in his eye, and says he's come all this way in the hope of getting laid.

I love his candour. I'm thinking he shouldn't have any difficulty.

He talks, and I listen, mind racing ahead, feeling confident. He tells me he's just bought himself a car, so at last he's been able to escape from the Godforsaken village where he lives, just up the coast from Oban. He'd like to get a job down here and move away for good but he hasn't the nerve to uproot. He supposes he's just a country boy at heart.

Later he offers me a lift home in his new car.

'So, it was about that time when his aunt took ill in Glasgow,' Rab was saying. 'Of course, none of us knew he even had an aunt in Glasgow; but she'd written, seemingly, to say she needed someone to look after her at weekends. So off he went, every Friday in that car of his, as regular as clockwork, and back on the Sunday night.' He leaned forward suddenly and laid a heavy hand on the young man's arm. 'Mind you,' he confided, 'I'd my own theories about this "aunt". If you ask me it was a fancy woman he was going away to see.' He pondered for a moment and then said, 'Of course, you'll maybe know.'

'Know what?'

'If he had an aunt in Glasgow.'

The young man shook his head. 'I don't remember him mentioning an aunt.'

'Well, there you are then!' And Rab sat back with a self-satisfied grin on his face.

Kisses. Warm, long kisses that start on Friday nights and last till Sunday. The wet softness of his lips, the smoothness of his cheek, and his ear, like a wax flower. I could lie here forever, stroking his silk strands of hair.

I want to tell him I love him but I daren't. He is too young to be smothered, too mercurial to pin down. Maybe he knows anyway: inferring it from the way I cradle his head.

Later, I allow myself to say that I love making love to him. He slides out from under me and paces the room, his lithe body looking even more appealing in the semi-darkness, the half-light from the window back-lighting his fluffy curls like a halo: Mother Nature's Son. He says maybe I'm getting too fond of him; he doesn't want to be tied to anyone so soon. I agree, but I'm aching inwardly. Why can't he feel the way I do; why can't he stay here permanently?

Smiling, he engulfs me again, and we resume our embrace; but after he's gone I find myself crying.

'So, how did you come to meet Donald?'

'Sorry . . ?'

'You and Donald,' repeated Rab. 'How did you meet?'

'Oh, he used to come into my local when he was down in Glasgow. We got talking . . . you know how you do. We found we had a lot in common.'

'You play the pipes then, do you?'

'No, no. We went to the art gallery together. He liked the same kind of paintings as me.'

Rab looked at him over his pint mug. 'Paintings, eh? Now, I never knew Donald paid much heed to paintings. And he never mentioned his aunt?'

'No, I don't believe he did.'

Rab shook his head slowly.

'And a woman? Was he never with a woman?'

'Not when I saw him,' confirmed the young man.

The gallery's quiet. We're standing in front of the Dali Christ, and he says at last here's something he likes. I ask if he's religious, and he admits to never having forgiven God for taking away his parents.

I show him the other Dalis, the plastic watches in the desert, and he pronounces them rubbish. Let's go and have a drink somewhere. We linger over coffees and I start to tell him about the film I saw on Wednesday; he reminds me he's already heard about it. There's nothing more to talk about so we go home to bed.

In the dark I try to memorise his body with my fingertips. We have established a routine but I can control the timing. Sensing this may be the last time, I slow down our rhythm. When at last our bodies shudder in synchronised crescendos, I find tears welling to the surface. He asks what's wrong.

They say one partner always loves the other more. I know I'm losing him. I wipe my face against the pillow and say, 'Nothing.'

'You used to hear him practising on that chanter well into the small hours.' Rab stopped. 'Are you all right, lad?'

The young man was taking a sip of his drink, and his hand was shaking so much it seemed unlikely the glass would ever reach his mouth. His face had turned ashen and had such an agonised look that Rab was beginning to think it had all been a bit of a shock for him. 'Look, Davy'll make you a cup of tea I daresay, or you can have another drink if you'd rather.'

'Thanks,' said the young man, pushing his glass towards Rab. 'I'll have another of these.'

He watched the farmer thread his way over to the bar, regretting his decision to call here en route to Inverness. When Donnie had stopped his weekend visits to Glasgow they had simply lost touch. Now he wished he'd kept it that way. There was a certain amount of truth in the concept of blissful ignorance.

Rab returned with their respective glasses recharged and reinstalled himself in his chair.

'I suppose the old aunt recovered?'

'No, she died, Donnie said. Mark you, he seemed more relieved than upset.' He chuckled. 'I think his ladyfriend most likely gave him the heave-ho; but I suppose we'll never know for sure.'

The young man suddenly threw back his drink. 'Some things it's better not to know,' he declared, standing and picking up his bag. 'Thanks for talking to me.'

Rab nodded and watched him move between the tables towards the door. He sipped his drink deliberately, still watching in case for any reason the young man should take it into his head to return.

Then he caught the eye of the barman, and Davy opened the door into the back kitchen.

'Are you there, Donald?' he called out. 'If you're not doing anything you can give us a hand with these glasses. Your friend's away.'

GRAEME WOOLASTON

GRAEME WOOLASTON

wolf by moonlight

Don Hendrie is a Glasgow-born architect, resident in southern England, in his mid-fifties. Convalescing from a heart attack, he is persuaded by archaeologist friend Sarah Neville to take a fortnight's break in Balcorrie in the East Neuk of Fife while she is on a dig. Balcorrie was where Don's family spent the summer holidays of his childhood.

Before leaving, he arranges with his young friend Alan Maitland to meet there during his stay. Learning of the dig, Alan tells him of a one-night stand with a student archaeologist called Phil.

The dig is focused on the Balcorrie Stone, a Pictish monument which is going to be incorporated into a visitors centre. Sarah's colleagues are Scottish archaeologist Stephen Harris, whose wife is due to give birth to their first child imminently, and Phil Owen, one of her research students. Don soon begins to suspect he is the Phil that Alan mentioned.

Shortly after his arrival, a poster informs him that Ewan Robertson, a star in a TV soap, is going to visit the village to open a community centre. Don had an affair with Ewan 15 years previously, when he was a young actor in the local rep. He still videos every episode of the soap for the opportunity to see him again.

The following morning Don again went to the old shop to buy his paper. Today there was a change to it: Ewan grinned to him in the porch and from behind the counter. As he waited to be served he wondered if he might not take a trip out of Balcorrie on Saturday; maybe go to St Andrews for the day.

The morning was overcast but dry, and he read his paper in comfort at the vantage point above the harbour. Then he struck off towards the kirk and the cemetery, but walked beyond them and past the tourists photographing the Balcorrie Stone till he came to the field further along the hollow where the archaeologists were at work.

Phil was on his hands and knees in a shallow trench surrounded by trays and sieves and plastic bags. It was the first time Don had seen him in working clothes; he couldn't decide whether the stained T-shirt and dirty jeans spoiled his prettiness or made him attractively rough.

Phil sat back and grinned: 'Want to give a hand?'

'Maybe not today! What are you looking for here?'

'Oh, we archaeologists don't look *for* anything. We just look.' He laughed, and resumed trowelling.

Don heard Sarah calling him: 'Come and see our research lab,' she shouted across. She led him to a workmen's wooden hut in a corner of the field: 'Sumptuous, ain't it? It's on loan from the council.'

The interior reminded him of a garden shed: there was a strong smell of creosote, shelves which looked extremely unstable, and one grubby window. Below it Stephen was sitting at a workbench, examining pieces of dark pottery.

'This is fascinating,' he said without looking round. Don couldn't suppress a giggle.

'Oh – hi!'

'I didn't mean to be rude, but I'm always amused by the way you people react to bits of pots – the fact that you can get more excited about a broken jug than about the Stone out there.'

from **wolf by moonlight** 227

Stephen smiled: 'That's because a broken jug can sometimes tell us more than a symbol stone.'

'Well, I can see the truth of that.'

Stephen began to show him some of the fragments and explain their dates and likely places of origin. Don listened politely, but he was more interested in the brown hair protruding above the neckline of Stephen's T-shirt. Once again he was conscious of the contrast between the excellence of his figure and the plainness of his features; all the same, he thought, if I'd had to work with a pair like him and Phil, sexual frustration would have given me a coronary years ago.

'Why don't I take you on a tour of the site?' Sarah suggested.

For the next 20 minutes she showed him the field, now once again growing barley, where she and Stephen had worked the previous season, and the much larger area the three of them were investigating this year.

'Dear God!' Don exclaimed. 'The damned visitors centre isn't going to cover all this, is it?'

'Yes – remember, there'll need to be a substantial car park. Surely you of all people can judge that for yourself?'

She was right; a facility of the size proposed would easily disturb the entire field.

'Couldn't you fake a discovery that would make it impossible for anyone to build here?' He looked across to the Stone: 'God, I hate the idea. The whole impact of the Stone will be ruined. Is it really going to be enclosed inside the centre?'

'I'm afraid it has to be, because otherwise it'll be lost altogether – there's been an alarming deterioration in the carvings in the last 20 years.' She looked beyond him: 'Oh, here's Stephen – you can ask him about it.'

'I was just complaining to Sarah,' Don said when he joined them, 'about the Stone being put indoors. It's sad to think this is the last summer we'll be able to see it properly.' He looked towards the encroaching houses and pulled a face: 'Mind you, a lot of the atmosphere here has already been destroyed. When I was a kid the Stone was wonderful, standing all on its own. Eerie, even.'

'Stephen's an authority on symbol stones,' Sarah remarked. 'Have you got time to take Don over the carvings here?'

'I'd be happy to – I've come out for a breath of fresh air. I think I'm getting high on the smell of creosote in that hut.'

Sarah went to rejoin Phil while Don and Stephen opened a gate which gave access to the area of neatly trimmed grass around the Stone. Almost three metres high, bending as if it had been twisted by the winds of centuries, it towered above them as Don peered to see the symbols Stephen was describing. He quickly realised Stephen was on to a favourite subject and that he was going to learn a great deal more about Pictish art than he had ever cared to know. Crescents, V-rods, double discs, Z-rods, mirrors and combs ran through Stephen's talk before he came to the carvings at eye level of warriors and beasts, including an instantly recognisable outline of a long, lean wolf.

As his attention wandered, Don realised Stephen had attracted a second audience of two French girls. He caught a fragment of their whispered conversation:

'C'est un prof, bien sûr?'

'Non, il est trop beau pour être prof.'

'T'as peut-être raison. Il est vraiment vachement beau.'

Don tried to conceal the astonishment with which he looked at Stephen again. 'Really handsome?' Was he missing something? 'The wolf's fantastic, isn't it?' he said absent-mindedly.

Stephen was delighted. 'Yes, it's absolutely realistic. You see how its ears are up and its tail is high – that's the sign of a dominant wolf, the leader of the pack. Whoever carved this had clearly observed the behaviour of wolves in the wild.'

The French girls distracted Don's attention again. One of them appeared to be about to photograph the Stone when at the last moment she moved her camera to the right and instead took a shot of an oblivious Stephen, who was now on to the differences between symbol stones and Christian cross slabs. She lowered her camera and instantly saw that Don had observed her ruse. She started to blush;

but Don grinned and nodded to her, causing both girls to giggle. At last Stephen became aware of their presence.

'They wonder if you're a teacher,' Don said.

'Eh? No – archaeologist,' he said, and mimicked digging with a spade.

'You are on the excavation here?' the girl with the camera asked. 'What do you hope to find?'

'I'll leave you to the visitors,' Don said. 'I've taken up enough of your time as it is – many thanks.'

'Not at all – I enjoyed it.' I know you did, Don thought. Stephen walked off with the girls, both of whom spoke excellent English, though Don wondered if it was up to coping with Stephen on eighth-century Picts. But he had a feeling they wouldn't care.

He was glad of the opportunity to look at the Stone again in peace. What fascinated him about it as an adult was exactly what had fascinated him as a child: its size and its rough-hewn, twisted shape. The carvings were of little interest to him, except the wolf. There was no doubt Stephen was right that it was carved from life; he'd seen wolves in nature documentaries on TV and they looked exactly like this. He glanced round to make sure he was still alone. A party of tourists was approaching rapidly, but they were far enough away for him to risk disobeying the large notices forbidding visitors from touching the carvings. He put his finger into the groove of the wolf's outline and drew it slowly along the 20-centimetre length of the animal's back. As he did so he had an impulse to whisper to it: 'You are beautiful!' But the tourists were now upon him, talking with American accents. He turned to leave.

Don lunched in a pub again. Since he had been at the Stone the cloud cover had broken and the day was becoming hot; pondering what to do, he remembered there was a clifftop walk to another village, smaller than Balcorrie but just as attractive, about three miles north. Since the walk involved no steep climbs it wouldn't be strenuous, and he could rest over another pint before returning.

The afternoon proved as good as he had hoped it would be. By the time he reached Balcorrie again it was gone five o'clock, and either because of the exercise, exposure to the sun, or the effect of the sea air, he felt healthier than he had done at any point in his recovery. Maybe Sarah had been right about the intrinsic benefits of coming here.

He paused on the cliff edge high above the beach. The tide was out, and the sand looked irresistible. He clambered down a path, found a spot that looked clean and comfortable, and sat down to gaze at the sea.

After a minute he was startled by a shout from behind him: 'Hi there!' He twisted round to see Stephen and Phil, each carrying a bag. As they approached he had time to notice again the contrast in their appearances: Stephen tall and lean, with long hair, and Phil much shorter – he scarcely reached Stephen's shoulders – with neatly cut hair, and a hint of plumpness. As in the pub last night, he felt an illustrated dictionary could have used them to explain the difference between 'hunky' and 'cute'.

'You've finished early, haven't you?' he asked when they reached him.

Stephen put his bag down: 'No, we've got to go back and do some more recording, but we decided to have a swim while the afternoon's still hot. We reckon we need it.'

'Too right!' Phil said. 'You don't want to be near us till we've been in the water.'

Stephen opened his bag and produced a tartan rug which he spread out on the sand. Then in one swift motion he pulled off his T-shirt; Don found himself looking up at a torso which seemed to be pure sinew decorated with chestnut hair. Within seconds Phil's shirt too was lying on the rug.

Don focused on the sea. He was aware of Stephen struggling out of his boots and socks; a moment later he was dropping his jeans. Don couldn't resist looking up again. He didn't know whether or not he was relieved to see that Stephen was already wearing swimming shorts. Phil's jeans fell onto the rug; he too was in shorts.

from **wolf by moonlight** 231

'Good God!' Don exclaimed. 'You've come prepared, haven't you?'

Stephen laughed: 'We always get changed in the site hut – saves one hassle with towels, at least.' He pushed his hair behind his ears: 'Don, are you planning to be here for a while?'

'I imagine so, yes.'

'You couldn't keep an eye on our clothes for us, could you?'

'Not a problem.'

Stephen grinned to Phil: 'Are you going to be a wimp again about going in?'

'Yes!'

They ran together towards the sea, but while Stephen at once plunged beneath the surface Phil walked in, bobbing up and down when the water reached his shorts and only then striking out. Soon they became no more than dark heads in the brightness.

Well, there goes the rest of my relaxing afternoon, Don thought; to see either of those two in swimming gear would be bad enough, but both of them together . . . *Vachement beau* remained a mystery, but he was beginning to understand why Sarah talked about 'sexy Stephen'. His shorts had revealed gorgeously hairy legs – oh, stop it, stop it, he told himself. Think about something else – think how cold that water is. He wondered just how many hours he and Neil had spent paddling here when they were boys. But he couldn't recall, nor could he even imagine, wanting to go further and start swimming. However, the two figures, splashing about noisily, were clearly enjoying themselves; as he watched them he was reminded of Ewan, but on much hotter days and in much warmer seas.

A phone began to ring. Automatically his hand went to his pocket, before he remembered his mobile was back in the hotel. He looked round to see where the noise was coming from: apparently the heap of clothes in front of him. Of course, Stephen's mobile. Was Sarah trying to reach him? Was it worth getting him out of the water?

Then he remembered the reason Stephen had given for carrying his mobile at all times.

Instantly he was on his feet and running down to the water's edge:

'Stephen! Stephen!' he shouted, but only on the fourth or fifth attempt managed to catch his attention. He made the gesture, with thumb and little finger, of holding a phone to his ear. At once Stephen struck out for the shore, shouted a brief 'Thanks' as he ran past, picked up his jeans and ripped the now silent mobile out of the pocket. There was a series of beeps as he pressed buttons. Then he dropped the jeans and burst out laughing.

Don went up to him: 'What is it?'

'I told her not to do this! I told her a thousand fucking times! I'll fucking wring her fucking neck!' – but he was still laughing.

'Not major news, then?'

'Not at all. She's left a message to remind me that the day after tomorrow is my brother's birthday. Aaargh!' He laughed again as he bent to put the phone back into his jeans pocket. 'Christ, that nearly gave me a heart attack out there.' He twisted round: 'Oh – Don, I'm sorry . . .'

Don was too distracted by the clinging of his shorts to his buns to be offended: 'Don't worry.'

By now Phil had joined them: 'False alarm,' Stephen said. 'Just Janice reminding me to buy a fucking birthday card!' He straightened up and looked towards the sea. Broken lines of water trickled down his back; thicker streamlets ran down his thighs from his shorts.

'Aren't you cold?' Don asked.

'I will be if I hang around – I'm going in again. Coming?' he asked Phil.

'No, I've had enough.'

'English wimp!' – and he was off to the sea.

Phil bent to get a towel out of his bag. Dear God, Don thought, much more of this and I'll be lucky if I see sundown. Phil's remarks as he straightened up didn't help: 'He's a bit of a fitness fanatic, that one – goes jogging whenever he gets the chance, as well as swimming. I tell you, he's changed my lifestyle in a week – he practically bullies me into joining him in that freezing water every day! And he plays rugby.'

'Really? He doesn't look the type.'

Phil rubbed his hair: 'In what way?'

'I'd have thought he had too slim a build.'

Phil didn't react.

Don was in a quandary; it was absurd for him to remain standing, so he sat on the sand again. But now he was looking up at Phil, whose head for the moment had disappeared inside his towel. What was left in view was, quite simply, delightful.

This was the opportunity he had hoped for, to get Phil alone so he could quiz him about Alan. But the circumstances couldn't have been more awkward. However, he had no option; there might not be another chance.

'Phil – I think we may have an acquaintance in common, back home.'

His head reappeared: 'Oh?'

'Yes. A guy called Alan Maitland. Works in finance management.' God, how to put it? 'He mentioned to me that he knew a Phil in the university archaeology department – he may have met you about six months ago?'

Phil stopped drying his shoulders: 'Oh. Oh – yes, Alan Maitland. Yes, I remember.'

The two men gazed at each other. From his eyes and his expression Don realised Phil wasn't surprised by what had just been revealed. Rather it was himself who was surprised; Phil must have understood the context of Sarah's banter in the pub after all.

He looked away: 'I've known Alan for eight years, since he was a student. We're just friends – nothing else.'

He turned to Phil again. He had moved his towel to his chest, as if screening himself: 'I only met him once, at a party. He was about to go off for a month's holiday.'

'Yes, to America.'

'That's right. I wanted to get in touch with him when he got back, but I lost the note of his number. I thought I'd see him around on the scene, but I haven't. Mind you, I'm not a great fan of our local scene.'

'Neither is he.'

Phil sat down and leaned forward to dry his legs.

'Phil – he's coming to Balcorrie. I'm not sure exactly when. He's on a touring holiday, and he's going to ring me to let me know his plans.'

'Really?'

His tone revealed nothing.

'He's planning to stay for a night – in our hotel, if there's a vacancy. It's very likely that you'll meet him.'

'That'll be okay.'

'I need hardly say he'll be totally discreet.'

Phil stood up and put the towel round his middle; his hands struggled at his waist and then at his knees as he pulled down his shorts. Don gazed out to sea again, conscious of Phil drying himself: 'So, what's he up to these days?'

Don assumed he understood the question.

'Nothing very new. Just going on like before.'

'He seemed' – Phil stopped. Taken by surprise, Don looked up at him. For the first time since the conversation had become serious he smiled: 'He gave me the impression he's not a guy who likes getting tied down too much.'

Don grinned: 'That's the way of it.' Phil resumed drying his upper legs; once again Don turned towards the sea.

'What about yourself?' he asked. 'How does life treat you?'

'Oh, very much the same. I used to have a regular boyfriend, but nowadays . ..' He laughed: 'I haven't been tied down for ages.'

'I take it Sarah and Stephen don't know about you?'

'Certainly not officially. I think Stephen's got an idea, though.'

'Why?'

'Well, he never says anything to me about women or girls or anything. That's how you can usually tell when a straight guy's clued up.' He sat down; Don felt he could relax from staring forward till he saw Phil pull a pair of white briefs out of his bag. He looked away again.

'But if he does know,' Phil went on as he struggled with his pants, 'it certainly doesn't seem to bother him. He's not at all inhibited in our room – pads around in the buff quite happily when he's off for a shower, and so on.' Instantly Don pictured the scene; he tried to suppress the image. 'Maybe being a rugby player, he just doesn't think twice about it.' The image recurred. Phil laughed: 'Of course, it means I have to do the same, otherwise I'd look like the sort of tube who wears swimming trunks on a nudist beach.'

The image returned yet again, now with an added player; for the third time Don struggled to reject it.

But the extra player was next to him, laying aside his towel and standing up, and he couldn't stop himself turning to look. He was at once disconcerted to see Phil gazing down as if he had expected this. For several seconds he didn't move, though his briefs, unlike his shorts, made his packet starkly obvious. Oh Christ, Don thought, please don't tell me you're a cock-teaser? He was relieved when Phil stooped for his jeans: 'Still, it could be worse.'

'Sorry?'

Phil began to turn back into a dirt-stained archaeologist: 'It would have been awkward if I'd fancied him.'

'Don't you?'

'Christ, no – he's far too hairy for me.' He glanced down with a sly mischievousness: 'From top to bottom – so to speak.' He went on as Don laughed: 'I've even started taking the piss out of him about it – I tell him the reason he doesn't feel the cold of the water as much as me is because he's got a lot more insulation.' He zipped himself up; 'How about you – do you fancy him?'

The directness of the question astonished Don, till he remembered that Phil was at an age when subtlety was an art still to be learned. Then he realised there might be an advantage in exaggerating: 'Oh, he's very much the type of guy I go for.'

'Really?'

The word was said with such scepticism Don started to laugh: 'Yes, really.' Again he chose to overstate: 'I think he's an absolute hunk.'

Phil stared at him as if he was incredulous. Then he sat down and began to pull his socks on: 'How long have you known Sarah?'

'About 15 years.'

'She's terrific fun to work for.' He laced up his boots: 'That TV guy you and her were talking about last night – I take it you and him . . .?'

So Phil had indeed understood the code of their conversation: 'Yes.'

'Special, was he?'

Once again Don realised that, for Phil, delicacy lay in the future: 'Oh, yes. Yes, very much.'

Phil nodded: 'So I gathered. Bit of a bummer him turning up to spoil your holiday, isn't it?'

Now Don was resentful: 'I've no intention of letting him spoil my holiday. Oh, here comes Stephen.'

Within seconds he was above them, stooping for his towel: 'You shouldn't give up so easily, Phil. Once you get used to it, the water's fine.' He began rubbing his chest. 'What are you two smiling about?'

'I've been explaining to Don my theory about why you don't feel the cold out there.'

Stephen swiped his towel towards him: 'Cheeky little runt!' Phil dodged sideways: 'I tell you, Don, in the mornings I can have my breakfast while he's still waiting for the shower to get through to his skin' – he dodged to the other side as Stephen swiped at him again, and then leaned back on his elbows, still shirtless, grinning at his own joke.

Don looked from him to the wet Stephen: was Phil kidding himself that he didn't admire that taut physique? But if Stephen had any inkling he was being flirted with – and surely he had – his smile suggested no reaction except, perhaps, a passing enjoyment of the sense of his own sexiness.

'Thanks for looking after our stuff,' he said.

'It was nothing.'

Don decided he had to resist the temptation to stay on and witness another display of the art of changing below a towel; he stood up and brushed the sand off the seat of his trousers: 'It's time I was heading home. I'm taking Sarah out this evening to the Italian restaurant in the High Street.'

'Well, enjoy yourselves!'

Back at the hotel there was no doubt about his most urgent physical need. He drew the curtains, undressed, lay on the bed, and began to let his mind play over what he had seen on the beach and what, concealed there but so easy to imagine, was seen daily in the adjoining room. If only the wall contained a two-way mirror! He came very quickly.

Once they were seated in the restaurant Don told Sarah about his afternoon, and about the *vachement beau* incident at the Stone. She hooted with laughter: 'God, in some ways he's so green, isn't he? I don't think he has any idea of the effect he can produce on people.' Don wasn't so sure, but it would be impossible to tell her why. Sarah carried on: 'Honestly, there's times in the pub when I think about getting him blind drunk and whipping him off to some remote western isle.'

Don shook his head as he laughed: 'I'm beginning to wonder if your interest in eighth-century Scotland hasn't more to do with Stephen than archaeology.' Suddenly a pun came to him: 'In fact' – he leaned across the table as he prepared to deliver it – 'more to do with *pecs* than *Picts*!' – he punched the air twice.

'Oh, God! Really, Don, your jokes' – but then much louder: 'Oh, for God's sake!'

She was looking at something beyond his shoulder: he twisted round. It took him a moment to realise what she'd seen: another copy of the photograph of Ewan among Festival posters on the wall. He turned back, smiling: 'That damn poster's breeding. It's turning up everywhere in the village.'

'Bloody hell! Have I got to sit and look at his moronic grin all through my meal?'

Don let the remark pass without comment. Why did she remain so resentful towards Ewan, long after his own bitterness had faded into little more than an intermittent sadness? Was it at all possible – he'd wondered about this before – that she was jealous of the role Ewan still had in his life?

'Don, to be serious for a moment – how do you think Stephen and Phil get on?'

He was instantly aware of delicacies.

'From what I've seen, they get on very well. Why do you ask?'

'To be honest, I was a bit nervous about bringing them together. They're very different from each other, don't you think?'

Even his friendship with Sarah didn't take precedence over maintaining Phil's confidence; if there was a subtext to the question he wasn't going to admit he'd noticed it.

'Well, Stephen's got family responsibilities, hasn't he?'

'It's not just that. Phil's rather – young for his age, don't you think? While Stephen's the exact opposite. He can be a bit heavy at times.'

Don was glad to divert the conversation away from what he still suspected Sarah might be asking: 'Like, on the subject of Pictish art.'

She laughed: 'Oh, certainly.' She came back to her first point: 'All the same, they seem to rub along together well, don't they?'

The inadvertent *double entendre*, particularly obvious to him after his pre-dinner activities, made him burst out laughing: 'Why shouldn't they?'

He saw she was relieved: 'Of course! Why shouldn't they?' She picked up the menu: 'Christ, I'm ravenous. Are you going to have a starter?'

'Well, I don't know if I dare. It might reduce my life expectancy even further.' She looked at him with horror: 'Oh, Sarah! I walked six miles this afternoon, no bother – maybe I'm in better shape than I thought.'

SEBASTIAN BEAUMONT

SEBASTIAN BEAUMONT

squat

David was told, later, that ditching your lover is one of the things that people *do* when they start at university – a kind of shrugging off of the past, a way of emerging from the chrysalis of home life. But early October was unseasonally warm and David felt enervated and dizzy after he'd sent the letter, when actually he'd hoped to feel a new sense of freedom.

On the evening of the posting, he went to one of the campus bars and found that, after his third pint, he became wildly emotional with what he thought of as 'misery' but which had, at its core, an exhilaration that made his eyes sparkle. He contemplated suicide. He contemplated shutting himself away, hermit-like, for the three years of his course. He contemplated having a tragic love affair that would end after he'd drowned in the sea whilst trying to save his boyfriend from a fearsome undercurrent (he would succeed in the rescue but sacrifice his own life in the process – his body being washed up days later, the expression on his face, in death, hauntingly beautiful).

How the conversation with Tom started, he could never remember, but that was his state of mind when they met – semi-hysterical melancholy. Tom had, by chance, been ditched that day by his girlfriend. He'd received her letter that morning. He took it from his

240

pocket and passed it to David – the wording was eerily similar to the letter that David had written. It seemed weird, psychic almost, but then, David thought, how many ways *are* there of saying these things?

It was his first real conversation since starting at university and David ended up back in Tom's room, drinking home brew and talking about 'relationships'. Even though he was drunk, David knew that Tom's suffering was real and his own was not. Tom had received rather than sent bad news and it showed in his dull movements, his curious sighs and his yearning for things to have turned out differently. David hadn't even been in love with his boyfriend and knew that he had been right to break off with him.

In the morning he vaguely remembered being sick in Tom's sink and having to be helped back to his room in halls. He woke feeling better than he had any right to. In a small part of himself he felt empty and dissipated, whilst at the same time another, larger part had settled in some indefinable way.

He was lying in bed preparing to succumb to the need to clean his teeth when there came a banging on his door. There was a mirror above his small desk and as he crossed the cool linoleum he noticed that his hair was a mess, he needed a shave and his eyelids had the subtle sheen that precedes the bruised look of exhaustion. He smiled at himself. He looked as though he'd been scared by the intensity of life.

'Okay, okay,' he called as he pulled on a pair of jeans and a T-shirt before opening the door.

It was his brother.

Mick was in his third year. His presence in Edinburgh had almost made David decide not to come, but the flexible English degree here suited him so well that he'd reckoned it was worth it. He liked Mick, but David had always been wary of his brother's charm. At home, Mick had overshadowed him, was more popular with everyone. He had that ability – awesome to those who do not possess it – of being able to make friends effortlessly. David's shyness and diffidence meant that he was a loner and this, coupled with his homosexuality, soured his relationship with his parents, especially his father, who wanted him to be easy-going and 'normal', like Mick.

David and Mick had travelled up for the start of term together and Mick had shown him round the campus, but they'd hardly seen each other since then, which pleased David who was determined that his brother should not overshadow his new life.

'Got any coffee?' Mick asked when he came in.

He sat on David's bed and then lay back with a sigh.

David put the kettle on and brushed his teeth whilst Mick closed his eyes. When he put the mug of coffee by the bed, Mick sat up.

'Haven't been to sleep yet,' he said. 'I'm still wired.'

David had known that his brother took drugs, at least occasionally, from oblique references he'd made at home, but he'd never seen Mick 'wired' before. He looked pale, and thinner, somehow, and lighter – as though he might inadvertently levitate from the bed – and his eyes looked wide and innocent and knowing.

There came a light tapping on the door. Mick looked at David and raised his eyebrows slightly.

It was Tom.

'I just wanted to check that you were okay after last night,' he said.

'Fine,' David told him. 'I'm fine. Come in and have some coffee. This is my brother, Mick.'

There followed a disjointed and rather surreal conversation which ended up with the three of them drinking beer once more back in Tom's room. As soon as Mick had finished his second glass he passed out, slumped and oddly immobile, in the one easy chair in the room. David and Tom left him there and went for a walk.

'Your brother seems a nice guy,' said Tom.

David made a noncommittal noise and changed the subject.

It was the last warm day of the year. Tom drove them up to Dunsapie Loch and they walked from there up the tussocky slope of Arthur's Seat, where they wandered over the worn rocky summit and looked out at the great bank of cloud that was looming from the west. Tom had also just started his studies. English and Medieval Scottish

History. Their courses overlapped and for one course they shared the same tutor, a modernist whose intellect had both frightened and inspired David at their first and, as yet, only meeting.

'He's cool,' said Tom. 'I don't want someone who refers to the classics all the time.'

They talked in an eclectic, random way. Tom had a hesitant manner and admitted that he was naturally shy, having only managed a conversation with David the previous evening because he was already drunk. David laughed at this and admitted that he was also pleased to have broken his solitude.

Their friendship fell into place without thought or apparent effort and it wasn't long before they were meeting every day for coffee or a drink. Tom was introspective and occasionally moody or, more difficultly, silent, but David, who had never been particularly gregarious, welcomed a friendship that had an intellectual rapport to it as well as everything else he might have hoped or expected from a friend. Tom encouraged David to read writers such as Jack Kerouac, Kurt Vonnegut Jnr and Aldous Huxley, whilst David introduced Tom to Alain Fournier and Hermann Hesse. They argued about E.M. Forster, who David thought too mannered, and D.H. Lawrence, who Tom thought pretentious.

David's course work went well, his tutor was pleased; Mick made fun of him, saying that the first year was for pissing about, not working. But David was happy. He'd never had a friend before with whom he could argue, go for walks, laugh and get drunk. Tom didn't seem bothered by the fact that David was gay, and as David wasn't attracted to Tom, sexually, it was never an issue, except occasionally in the snide remarks Tom received from the 'lads' on his course for having a gay friend.

As a pair it was somehow easier to get to know others and David began to feel more and more settled into the routine of university life. During the Christmas holidays, David spent a week with Tom's family, which seemed to cement their friendship.

In March, Tom started an affair with a young woman called Stella, a second-year psychology student. Stella wore dark make-up, long dresses, Doc Marten's and lived in a squat on the edge of Newhaven and the Leith docks with two other students. She was loud, opinionated and clearly smitten by Tom, whose pale, wholesome face became radiant when they were together. Inevitably, during the first month that Tom was with Stella, David hardly saw him at all. When they did meet, Stella was hostile. David wanted to tell her that he posed no threat to their relationship, but didn't know how to say it, and so, instead, he began to avoid her.

In the vacuum left by Tom's absence, David made the mistake of falling into an affair of his own with someone on his course – Fergus, an intense, dreamy boy with curly dark hair and brooding eyes. He had been floating at the periphery of David's life for some time, but David hadn't particularly noticed. Now, with so much time on his hands, it seemed inevitable that they would sleep together, which they did. It was successful, in a way. Physically, they 'clicked', but David found it difficult to take Fergus's fanciful demeanour seriously. He was too effusive about trivial things and had a collection of teddy bears that formed a mound on his bed.

As soon as David was perceived to have a boyfriend, Stella became more amiable and developed an interest in what he was reading. She liked Fergus, too, into whose room she would disappear to have private conversations, leaving Tom and David to chat.

But David's relationship with Fergus did not flourish. Sex was a balm of sorts, but it could not hide the gap between them, and when, one day, Fergus said, 'You hate my bears,' he had to admit that Fergus was right. Fergus smiled sadly at David and said, 'This isn't working, is it?' and David couldn't deny it. They avoided each other after that in a slightly embarrassed way.

In May, the two students that Stella shared her squat with moved on. Tom agreed to move in with her and when the three of them were in the refectory one afternoon he asked David if he wanted Stella's old room – the smaller bedroom at the back. Stella was obviously against it, but Tom had asked the question spontaneously without consulting her, and he had such a beguiling innocence to him that when he asked her 'Why?' she couldn't put her objection into words – though her expression was clear enough and her 'You keep your hands off my boyfriend' attitude made David partly want to laugh and partly to puke. 'Why?' he wanted to ask. 'Don't you believe that Tom is straight?' But he didn't say anything because he understood that although there might be some homophobic taint to her attitude, she also wanted to have Tom to herself and she resented the fact that there was some part of Tom and David's friendship that she could not share.

David went with Tom and Stella down to have a look at the room on offer to him. The street on which the house stood was a mess. On one side of the road was an area of waste ground. On the other, sandwiched in a short strip between the waste ground and the rear of a barbed-wire-protected warehouse, was a short terrace of houses in poor repair. Most of them were unoccupied. Those on either side of Stella's were standing but boarded up, though further along they were roofless or totally collapsed. The houses were part of the same plot as the waste ground and, as Stella explained, were corporately co-owned by two companies locked in argument as to what to do with it.

Once they were inside, Stella flicked on the light.

'At least we've got electricity,' she said, 'and running water.'

The sitting-room was sparsely furnished: a settee with a drape over it, a couple of ancient armchairs and a cheap stereo in the corner. The dining-room was uninhabitable because the floor had fallen in – likewise the bedroom above it. The third, smaller bedroom was watertight and painted a kind of dusty white, as though it had been whitewashed. It had bare floorboards, a rickety bed, a desk built of bricks and planks, and David loved it immediately.

Although there were occasional disturbances, and one attempted break-in, living there was a kind of idyll. Together, David and Stella cleaned up the house, particularly the kitchen, which was filthy and required some elementary plastering by the door. Although they knew they would be evicted at some point, no one seemed bothered that they were there, and so they continued as though this was a permanent arrangement.

David was pleased that he was getting on so well with Stella. He reckoned this was partly because of the amount of dope she was smoking. It seemed to have calmed her down, opened her up, made her less wary. Tom was smoking a lot, too, and David sometimes joined in, but he had a problem with drowsiness, and would often doze off, even after smoking only a little, so that in the end it began to seem rather pointless. This annoyed him as smoking dope fitted his idea of the lifestyle he saw himself as leading. He took relish in telling his parents he was living in a squat and laughed at their disapproval and their inevitable – and unfavourable – comparisons with Mick.

As spring gave way to summer it ceased to bother him that there was no back wall to the bathroom. He liked the fact that if he drew back the shower curtain he could feel a draught of cool, fresh air. Obviously it would be a problem in the winter if they were still here. But it was impossible to think that far ahead.

One of the customs of the squat, instigated by Stella's ex-housemates, was an 'open house' on Saturday nights when people would gather after the pubs had shut. David called them a 'dope brigade'. They would sit around until four or five in the morning talking and listening to music. David was polite to them, and sometimes joined in their conversations, but everything about them seemed to be distant and somehow impersonal. He was also aware of being resentful of the drug-fuelled camaraderie, because he wanted to be part of it, wanted to see himself as a cool dope smoker.

After a few weeks, David put a lock on his bedroom door.

'Why?' Stella asked him. 'Locks are so mistrustful, so alienating.'

'I've had five of my CDs nicked,' David told her. 'If you didn't have light-fingered friends, I wouldn't bother. I don't mind people listening to my music. I'd just rather they didn't steal it at the end of the evening.'

'He's right, Stella,' Tom told her. 'It's okay for us because we don't have any CDs to be stolen.'

'The reason why there's such a good atmosphere in this house is because it's so relaxed,' said Stella. 'Now David's changed that.'

'Nothing's changed,' David said. 'No one uses my bedroom except me. How can it have changed?'

'It's a question of trust, David,' she told him. 'You don't trust us anymore.'

After the summer term ended, David couldn't face going home. He stayed on in the house and went out to find work. Stella and Tom stayed too but without doing anything and began to run up spectacular debts.

David got a job as a bicycle courier. It wasn't something he'd ever imagined doing, but the money was better than any of the menial jobs that were on offer to students and, as he wasn't paying any rent, he found that, for the first time in his life, he had more money than he needed.

The first few days were exhausting, but as he began to get fitter he enjoyed it more and more, even in the wet weather that was becoming a hallmark of the summer, even in this city that was used to rain.

In the evenings, David would buy in some cheap bottles of beer or cider and sit up with Tom and Stella getting drunk and watching them smoke, and talking to the people that he began referring to as 'the faceless ones' who were coming round more and more often, not just on Saturdays. It was an easy, carefree time and he found that he could ignore Stella's hostility, which disappeared anyway when she was stoned. As he became fit, he drank less and continued reading his books, which he talked about with Tom, who had stopped reading altogether and was becoming gradually less and less communicative as the summer went on.

One day Tom asked David if he could borrow £100. David (who had saved up substantially more than that by then) agonised over a leisurely cup of coffee before refusing, saying, 'I share my beer with you every night. Isn't that enough? You want me to buy your dope for you too?'

'It's only a loan,' Tom said.

'Until when?'

There was no clear answer to that, so Tom didn't give one. David sighed, gave Tom £50 and said, 'Keep it. Don't give it back. It's a present.'

Stella started to become antagonistic again, and David felt guilty about having money when they didn't. Buying beer for the three of them to get drunk had somehow ceased to be enough of a contribution. He also started paying for basics like bread, sugar, tea, coffee and milk without complaint. They would simply run out of it if he didn't. It could sometimes be expensive. If half a dozen people came round, they would get through a jar of coffee in an evening.

Stella began to leave the room when David came in from work. She would go upstairs whilst David sat around in his cycling gear, drinking coffee with Tom and holding long, desultory and largely one-sided conversations. Stella wouldn't reappear until David went out to get the daily ration of beer – which he did promptly every evening at nine. He felt that if he started getting it any earlier, it would mark the start of some kind of inevitable decline.

'Don't worry about Stella,' Tom said one afternoon when Stella had left the room sighing particularly loudly, 'she's got a lot on her mind. It's not just you.'

Stella was cheerful, in a brittle way, when she was drunk, or dreamily carefree when stoned. But after so many weeks of rain, a leak had started in the corner of the sitting-room, and the quiet drip-drip of it seemed to David like the ticking of a time-bomb. The fact that none of them made any attempt to fix it was an eloquent statement about how much they had stopped being a committed household.

'Maybe I should move out,' David said to Tom.

'Don't,' said Tom. 'You're so good for us. I know Stella's being strange right now, but things will change.'

David reacted by buying himself a midi stereo system. He bought a second-hand armchair too, and spent most of his free time in his room listening to music or reading, and only occasionally coming down in the evenings for a beer and a chat with Tom. The fact that he stopped sharing his beer went unremarked, but people were calling round now on a nightly basis and Stella could always manage to cadge a can or two from visitors.

There was one guy, called Ian, who occasionally showed up with the others. He was quiet, but when he spoke he was thoughtful and interesting. David wasn't quite sure whose friend he was because he seemed to know everyone equally well – but then there was something detached about most of the people who came round so that no one appeared to be particularly connected with anyone else. Still, Ian seemed different. He always brought his own drink, for one.

Once, when David was in his room, Ian knocked on the door and came in. David was lying on his bed, reading.

'Hi,' Ian said, brandishing a bottle of cider and two glasses, 'can I sit down for a moment?'

David nodded and gestured towards the armchair.

'Stella can freeze people out at times,' Ian told him. 'Don't take it personally.'

He poured a drink and passed it over.

'Are you a student too?' David asked.

'I'm a trainee accountant,' he said and laughed. 'I know that sounds odd, given the friends I've got. But I find I'm growing out of them. That's odd, too, especially as I haven't grown into another set of friends yet, particularly not among the accountancy brigade, who are crackingly dull.'

They sipped their drinks in companionable silence for a while.

'Do you know Stella well?' David asked.

'When I did a lot of smack, Stella was good to me,' Ian said. 'Before she met Tom. The two guys she shared this house with were total smack-heads and I used to come round to shoot up. She somehow gave me an image of normality. She wasn't using smack herself, at least not then, and I used her as a kind of role model when I decided to come off it. She was brash and lively and not at all like the dull non-druggies in my family and at uni who were anything but a role model for getting clean. Although we weren't friends, she spent a lot of time with me when I gave up and I suppose I'll always owe her for that. But now that she and Tom are using it, I feel, well, not betrayed exactly, but sad. I know she's been trying to cut down for the sake of the baby, but . . .' He shook his head. 'I don't know. Who am I to judge?'

David felt a mournful welling of sorrow and he thought, why am I so blind?

'Where do they get it from?' he asked.

'That's never been difficult,' Ian said. 'At the moment there's this guy who calls himself "X", as though there's some great mystique to being a dealer. Mr fucking X.'

David didn't mention to Tom that he knew about the heroin. It just suddenly seemed appropriate that, for the first time that summer, he should go home to Castle Douglas for the weekend. He travelled back on Friday afternoon hoping for a rest from an existence that was becoming more and more confusing. But, once he was home, he couldn't relax. His old bedroom felt like someone else's. Considering he had so wanted to get away from Edinburgh, it shocked him how much he suddenly wanted to return.

His mother complained that he hardly ever phoned them, that he was becoming a stranger.

'I'm busy,' David told them. 'I've got a job.'

'You don't even go and see Mick now that his finals are over. And he's living in the same city as you.'

Mick had managed an Upper Second and, as far as David was aware, was signing on in Dalry.

'Okay, okay,' David said, 'I'll go and see him.'

He had a day of silences with his parents and cloying, unspoken criticisms and on Saturday evening he took the train north a day early.

His part of Edinburgh was dreary, but somehow in its cheerless gloom there was a kind of optimism, as though it was encouraging its children to rise above its squalor rather than be submerged by it. David bought a case of beer and walked back to the house in a light drizzle, thinking *I'll play this by ear. I'll try to understand this situation. Whatever else is true, Tom is still my friend.*

Back at the house, the waste ground was verdant because of all the rain. Inside, he could hear The Beloved playing quietly on the system in the sitting-room and was immediately wary – it was one of his own CDs that had been locked up in his room before he'd gone away. He put the beer in the hall and crept quietly upstairs to his bedroom. The door was ajar, splintered fragments of wood were hanging by the lock. He looked into the room. Everything was ordered, but his stereo was gone, his CDs were gone, his bike was gone . . .

He wasn't shocked. He was hardly even surprised.

He sat on the bed and wondered what to do. Part of him wanted to go downstairs and yell. Another part of him wanted to pack up his belongings and creep out of the house – a course of action he would have taken more seriously if he'd had anywhere to go. In the end he decided to walk calmly into the sitting-room and take it from there.

He paused outside the door for a moment, but there was only the quiet sound of music. He pushed the door open and stepped inside.

Stella, who was leaning back on the settee with Tom, looked up at him, opening her eyes lethargically, but not apparently recognising him. In the armchair – and here David was genuinely surprised – Mick was slumped, apparently asleep, a hypodermic needle on the floor below his hand, a loosened tourniquet still dangling below his bicep. The room was scented with incense, dope and the acrid smell of vomit.

'What's Mick doing here?' he asked Stella, who blinked a couple of times but didn't reply.

He crossed to Stella and knelt in front of her.

'Stella,' he said, slapping the back of her hand, 'Stella, what's going on? Where's my bike? Why's Mick here?'

'Mick?'

David pointed.

'My brother.'

'Mr X? Your brother?' she mumbled and then closed her eyes.

It was then that he noticed the vomit. Tom, who was slumped away from Stella, had been sick down the side of his shirt. His face was glistening with sweat, the stubble on his cheeks looked dark against his pale skin. David took his hand and slapped it, just as he had done with Stella.

'Tom,' he said. 'Tom . . .'

But there was no reply. David leaned forward, close to Tom's mouth, but he didn't seem to be breathing. He felt for a pulse but could feel nothing – he wasn't sure he was doing it properly, his own fingers were shaking so much.

An ambulance, he thought, and scrambled to his feet.

The phone box was on the corner at the top of the street and David misdialled before he got through. His breathing seemed remote to him and he found that he could hardly get the words out when he was asked which emergency service he required.

He sprinted back to the house in the rain. In the sitting-room the three of them were still immobile. The CD had stopped playing and all David could hear was the rain outside and the drip-drip-drip in the corner. Suddenly, David was on his knees, shaking Mick.

'Look what you've done,' he shouted. 'You've killed my friends, you shithead!'

Mick stirred, but without opening his eyes, then drifted off.

When the ambulance men arrived, David was still kneeling in front of his brother, shouting, 'You killed them, you killed my friends.'

Seven people died that night. It was all in the papers. Pure, uncut heroin had been sold to local dealers. No one had realised how strong it was, which was why so many people had overdosed on it. Mick was discovered to have four small baggies of the stuff on him and was arrested at the hospital. The papers called him a 'small-time criminal'. The main dealers were never caught. Stella, who survived, went to her parents' house. Tom was one of the seven who died.

One of the most vivid images from that night for David was of passing Mick at the police station, hours later, when he went in to make a statement. Mick was being taken to a cell and hissed at him, 'You called the *police*! You!' and David had whispered back, 'No, I didn't, I called an *ambulance*.' But Mick had already passed by then and didn't hear.

David stayed on alone in the empty house, bought another bike and worked longer and longer hours. The sun finally came out and his legs, arms and face became tanned whilst the rest of him remained pale. He lived on hamburgers and coffee and occasional beer. After a week or so, his parents came to get him. His mother was tearful and asked him to come home, but he told them to leave. His father tried to be strong and stern and reasonable, but David raised his voice slightly, turned his back, and his parents left, frightened by his quiet determination, and slipped a note under the door telling him to 'get in touch when you're ready'.

Someone came round from the city council about evicting him and he said, 'Fine, it's fine, I'll leave when I'm officially told to go.'

It was at the end of August that Ian found him, sitting wordlessly in the sitting-room. He was leaner, but clean and presentable as though he was about to go for a job interview. Ian sat beside him and took him in his arms and David cried for the first time.

'It was the money from my bike and my stereo that killed him,' he whispered.

When he had become silent and calm, Ian went upstairs, packed a bag for him and took him home to his flat in Newington.

It was the cycling that had kept him from cracking up completely. Now that he was staying with Ian, he worked more normal hours and went shopping every day, buying fresh vegetables and preparing recipes from Ian's selection of cookery books. They would share a bottle of wine over their evening meal, and then talk together or watch television. In the first week of September, David cycled past his old squat. The whole terrace had been sectioned off and demolition had begun. In mid-September Ian came home with the local paper. Mick had been sent to prison for nine months and the paper screamed at the inadequacy of the sentence.

'Go home,' Ian told him. 'It's time.'

Back in Castle Douglas, his mother was gentle and treated him as though he was convalescent. His father looked confused by what had happened and was unable to talk to his son. What had been such an ordinary family had become something else. Neighbours looked at David as though he was ill in some way, and possibly infectious. The papers revealed that Mick hadn't got a degree at all – he'd lied to everyone about his results.

There was an opportunity at the end of September for David to go and visit Mick, but Mick refused to see him. Instead, David lay in the garden and sunbathed. He read widely, from Sir Walter Scott to Iain Banks and felt that he understood the journey that each central character was taking. They started out in a position of stability, encountered a trauma or a crisis, coped with it, and in doing so became someone different. The books seemed to be describing the transformation of the human psyche through pain. He realised that the same had happened to him, but he was unsure in what way he had changed, only that change had happened. In the novels it all seemed to have a point, but for him there was no point and he realised that fiction is the imposing of structure on something that has no structure – an explanation of something that cannot be explained.

When it was time to return for his second year, David's mother gave him the battered Volkswagen Polo that she no longer used and he spent some of the money he'd saved over the summer to tax and insure it. He drove back to Edinburgh and accepted Ian's offer of a room in his house.

His year started in a dream. He had chosen – against his tutor's advice, because of the workload for a beginner – to do his minor course in the philosophy of literature, but it was good that he had something to immerse himself in. Everyone on his course knew that he was the person whose best friend had died of a heroin overdose and whose brother was a drug dealer. It gave him an aura that was at once impressive and distancing. David began to realise that if something extraordinary happens to you, it sets you apart.

Ian was wonderfully helpful. David would read his philosophy course work and then carefully explain it to Ian, who was an interested listener – taking some passages off to read for himself and then discussing them with David later. There was Marx and Materialism, a bit of Kant and Locke, Barthes' *Death of an Author* . . . It was over Foucault's theory of sexuality as constructed that they first kissed, a fact that would be referred to with humour thereafter. Hegel's ideas about ideal history were absorbed between bouts of lovemaking. How unmediated history cannot exist because all historians have an agenda was discussed whilst lying in bed and drinking post-coital coffee. Derrida's fluidity of meaning was deeply attractive to David. Somehow the concept of endless deferral of meaning made it possible to make almost anything of the past.

David was surprised that someone as beautiful as Ian could love him, and he accepted Ian's embraces with a desperation born of intense loneliness, only gradually accepting – with a kind of wonder – that Ian found him attractive.

Ian was six years older than David, slender and strong but clearly bruised by life. There was a vulnerability to him that David guessed was a hangover from his previous addiction, but his strength helped to make David stronger too. He claimed that David had helped save him from the terminal boredom of becoming an accountant and this statement made David feel valued.

David invited Ian home to Castle Douglas for Christmas. David's mother was clearly relieved that David was becoming respectable. Moving from a squat to live with an accountant-to-be met with her approval. Ian said later, 'I kept wanting to say, "Although I've never lived in a squat, perhaps you ought to know I used to be a heroin addict, Mrs McKenna".'

Back in Edinburgh for the spring term, David settled into his routine once more. Just before Easter, his personal tutor encouraged him to take a further course in philosophy in his final year as he was doing so well. Over Easter dinner in Castle Douglas, his father said, 'Yes, but what do you *do* with a degree in English and philosophy?' David wasn't thinking in those terms and couldn't answer his father's question. He might have been disturbed by this if he hadn't been more concerned by his mother's statement that Mick would shortly be coming out of prison.

Later, back in Edinburgh, Ian said, 'Of course, you know why you decided to take philosophy in the first place?'

'No,' he said.

'It's because you want to understand the nature of blame. You want to understand whose fault it is that Tom died. You want to understand whose fault it is that Mick's in prison, and why he blames you for the fact that he's there. You think you'll find the answer in Locke or Kant, or in the malleability of meaning proposed by Hegel and Derrida. But you won't. If you chase meaning in this way it will endlessly recede from you as surely as if you were running after the foot of a rainbow – you'll have the illusion that you're progressing towards a conclusion, but you'll never actually get there.'

'Where will I find answers then?'

'In your heart.'

David was too busy trying to meet a deadline to think about what Ian had said, though he recognised the statement as important and filed it away for further thought. The following day he delivered an essay titled: *Makers of Meaning: Textual Power and the Reader*. He knew it was good. He knew he would get a good mark for it. He drove home feeling contented and decided to stop and get an Indian carry-out at a place in town that was cheap and did a good bhuna.

As he was driving onto the Lothian Road a woman stepped out in front of the car. He hit her with his nearside wing and she went over the bonnet, smashing the windscreen with her full weight before falling off and hitting a stationary Land Rover. David braked hard and, when he'd stopped, he sat for several seconds looking at the blood that was smeared on the caved-in windscreen.

He got out of the car and there was already a small crowd gathering round the woman. People parted as he approached and as he looked down at her he could see that she was dead. Her neck was at an impossible angle. He turned and was sick in the gutter.

The police came, but David was in severe shock. He was questioned, but there was hardly anything he could say. He sat for hours in the police station before he could give them his number and they could phone Ian, who came straight over.

'It happened outside the off-licence by the Usher Hall,' the policeman told him. 'There were plenty of witnesses. The woman was drunk and had an argument with her boyfriend. He punched her and she ran into the road. Someone was going to hit her. It just happened to be this young man here.'

Ian helped David home where he locked himself in the bathroom and wouldn't come out.

'David,' Ian called, 'please, don't do this. Come out and let's talk about it.'

David didn't reply. He ran himself a bath and lay there looking at the ceiling. He noticed that the paint there was peeling slightly.

An hour later there was a tap at the door.

'David,' Ian called through the door, 'I don't want you to come out if you don't want to, but I'd like to ask you one thing. Please, unlock the door. I won't come in, I promise. It's just frightening me that it's so silent in there. If you unlock the door I'll leave you to your thoughts. If you don't, I'll break the door down.'

David sighed and turned his head. He looked at the door for some time. He had no recollection of having locked it in the first place. He leaned over and gently took the key in his fingers, turning it slowly so that it clicked in the lock.

'Thank you, David,' Ian whispered.

David woke, cold and stiff. It was dark and he couldn't see his watch. He felt exhausted and devoid of personality. It was strange, almost amusing, to discover that he could move his limbs. His arms were like those of a marionette. If he commanded them to move, they moved. He sat for a short time lifting and dropping his hands into the cold water and smiling at the oddness of it. Then he decided to get up. He stood slowly, his knees painfully stiff, his ankles numb, and sat on the edge of the bath for a while until he could move his feet properly. Then he walked slowly forward, out of the bathroom and, haltingly, to the bedroom. Ian was asleep on their bed with the bedside light on. He opened his eyes when David came into the room and raised his arms to him in a familiar gesture, and David stumbled forwards into them. Ian winced at the coldness of David's flesh and insisted that he take another bath to warm himself up. David had little recollection of this because he was so drowsy that he kept slipping in and out of sleep.

When he woke it was four o'clock in the afternoon. Ian was sitting by the bed. He smiled slightly as David opened his eyes.

David, as he remembered what had happened, thought, the words I say now will be the most important ones I ever speak. He didn't know why he thought this, but he knew that it was true. He closed his eyes and let his thoughts wander. He remembered the dark smudge of the woman's hair as her head collided with his windscreen. He remembered Tom's inert hand in his. He remembered Mick's pale face in the police station the night he was taken into custody.

He opened his eyes.

'Why have these things happened to *me*?' he asked.

Ian took his hand and held it silently.

from

everything you need

A.L. KENNEDY

Mary's bed wasn't really big enough for a couple to get much sleep. Mary had found a kind of rest, once she and Jonathan had giggled and rocked to their conclusions, but her mind had stayed open behind her eyes. She'd wanted to enjoy their lying and being coated in each other, sticky and slick, the sheet tugged back over them quickly translucent with sweat.

'Here you are, then, tea.'

The feel of being looked at – she'd known, for the first time, how very much she liked that. Drowsing now, she imagined she heard voices, but shook off the thought, the idea of being currently observed.

Nobody here, no bodies but us.

'Tea's the best thing, really. Isn't it?'

Any movement divided her from Jonathan uncomfortably, parted new adhesions, so they clung still and healed together, flesh to flesh, in one hot graft from their ankles to their scalps. Under the stone weight of Jonathan's arm, his thick breathing, her mind had shuddered with recollected skin, with the thought of the feel of fucking him.

Jonathan. Sleepy Jonathan. Sleeping Jonathan.
'Yes. Tea's best.'
Those voices . . .
Silly boy, sleeping and speaking. Daft. Lovelydaftlovelyshaftlovely.
'And cake.'
Recognisable voices.
'From Barr's – the good stuff.'
Goodlovelyshaft.
A little stirring of the house, a give in the mattress and Mary's heart bumped towards something more lively.
'Battenberg. Fresh.'
Her blood leaped, warily, but then eased back to let her picture the first dive of Jonathan's head, the stroke of his breath and his newly barbered hair, the pleasant realigning of her hips.
'Mary?'
Yes. That's me.
'I think she's still asleep, Butt. Will we leave it?'
'And he's asleep, too.'
Fuck.
She realised. She understood.
Fuck.
The Uncles were here.
They'd padded into her unbuttoned room. They were here with her now, speaking. Finally, their reality yanked her dumb awake.
'Ah, there now, Mary. What should we do?'
They stood, Morgan holding the tea tray, Bryn's hands holding themselves, and each man gently but plainly alarmed by the way they had chosen to proceed. Still, they were trying to do right by Mary, to let her feel at home and approved of, loved. She lurched up and opened her eyes to Bryn's face: his puzzled eyes fighting to not seem lost.
'What do you think? About where to put the tea? Oh, or Jonathan?'
Jonathan came to in a scrabble of panic, first trying to spring out of bed, then recoiling to cover himself with a small whinny of fear.

Morgan set down the tea tray on the bedside table, obscuring – perhaps intentionally – the two sloughed condoms lying there.

Everyone paused, unsure of how they might continue, and fell to staring at the willow pattern saucers and cups, the lumpily knitted tea cosy, the slices of buttered gingerbread and Battenberg. Each of them swallowed. Each of them tasted bedroom air, thick was the low-tide spatter of protein and the sweet, shellfish surfaces of Mary's privacy.

Bryn nodded through a carefully presented smile. 'We thought you might want a drink. Or a little to eat. We find that we do.'

'Afterwards.' Morgan drew away from the bed and back towards the door.

Mary and Jonathan lay rigid, sheet drawn to their chins, eyes dumbfounded, like a pair of bad Staffordshire figures – *The Lovers Apprehended.*

'It's as if . . .' Bryn pondered, also moving for the doorway, 'you'd been on a bus trip for a long time, so you're peckish. Something like that.' He blinked at Jonathan, his voice wavering, perhaps at the verge of laughter, perhaps only made unsteady by the strain of the occasion. 'We do wish you well.'

'We do.'

Mary finally found herself saying, 'I didn't know –'

'We were here. No.'

'We weren't. We had gone out. But then we came back.'

'Because you might need us.'

'You know.'

'We were here in case.'

As if they were taking their leave from royalty, Bryn and Morgan backed respectfully away.

'Mary?' Bryn waited until she turned to him, gave him her proper attention. 'We just wanted you to be comfortable. And, um, proud. Your first time should be something to be proud of, because you'll remember it. Perhaps this wasn't the best . . .' He huffed. 'Drink your tea, now, before it gets cold.'

And, because they might as well now, Mary and Jonno took tea.

from everything you need **261**

'Was that all right, then, with the Uncles?' Jonathan couldn't manage above a whisper yet.

'I think so. Yes. They say what they mean – so, yes.' She rocked against him, grinned. 'And it was all right with me, too.'

'Oh, good.' And he grinned as well.

The rattle of spoons and crockery in the warm, stunned room was making them feel a little as if they'd become, somehow, delicate, a pair of happy invalids. Then their appetites overtook them and they cleared the plate of cake, then worked crumbs and butter and marzipan and much more of themselves into the sheets.

But now that the Uncles were home, they lowered their voices – to show respect.

Mary made love to Jonno again on the 22nd of October, because it was her birthday.

'Thank you for the present.'

'Don't mention it.'

And then – avoiding the terrible Mother Davies – they managed again on the 27th, because they were both intoxicated by the terrible lack of time they still had left and because – having had five long, still days of reflection – they wanted to.

On the 30th they wanted to again because they were missing each other and Mary would be gone and because she'd passed Mrs Davies that morning in Bethel Lane and immediately needed more than anything, to be sliding along Jonno's cock, to be wet with him, and making him push his breath against her neck in a way that his mother, Mary guessed, could very probably not imagine.

On the 31st they did it by mistake because they had met to say goodbye – the Uncles out climbing the valley – and had both been intent on explaining to each other why having sex now would only make them sad. They had it anyway and *were* sad, but also wonderfully painstaking and intent. And this time, their last time, he could be naked in her: the round, silk push of him. Her period was only a day or so away, already tender in her breasts, and she could safely catch him up and have him all, live, to remember, to be really there.

Mary thought of Foal Island and, cooried warm beside all of Jonno's pulses, she felt increasingly cheap. Tomorrow she was leaving – no more Uncles, no more valley, no more Jonathan. A lock in her thinking turned, sold and surprising, and reminded her of what it frightened her to find she could still want, even her and even now.

Her new future hissed at her, made her blood bolt in a way she hoped that Jonno wouldn't notice, because it was secret, even from him: beyond simple, visible nakedness. This was what she stripped down to, beyond the bone, this odd, free emptiness. And she did believe that she wouldn't have to make herself lonely forever, she did feel she would, in the end, come back to Jonathan, live out her future gently with him here. But she was still going to leave him tomorrow. And that did still hurt.

She woke on the first of November, having failed to notice Halloween, and found that every detail of the house was waiting, ready to lacerate and cling. Her sheets breathed Jonno at her and were full of how quickly he showed he was pleased to be pleased. They reminded her of the temperature of his smile.

In the bathroom, here was the stupid pot with the blue plastic lid where Uncle Morgan's teeth swam their nights away and suddenly she liked it and wanted to see it regularly. His spare inhaler, his bottles of pills, the little daily fight to keep him breathing showed itself to her, inescapable. Bryn's 1,000-year-old dressing gown, hanging soft at the back of the door, she wanted to touch it, because it was almost him.

Downstairs in the kitchen, the Uncles were doing their best. They played with toast and jam and appeared to eat. They were immaculately brushed and soaped and shaved, both cleaned to an especially startled pink. Morgan's inhalations fretted more than usual under his cardigan.

'All right, then, girl? Thought you'd never get up.'
'I think I was tired.'

from *everything you need* 263

Bryn cradled his teacup, 'Well, no wonder.' He stared at the tablecloth – fresh on this morning, white with blue embroidered flowers. When she sat, he raised a grin to meet her, but couldn't quite persuade it to take.

Mary frowned back a burst of helplessness. 'I'm sorry.' Her voice waylaid her: was not as she intended, not firm, or cheerful, or strong.

'For what, love?'

'I don't know.' She caught herself back, imposed what she hoped was control. 'For all the time . . . I've been too much with Jonathan. I should have spent more time with you.'

Bryn's hand muffled down over hers, his skin always finer than she remembered. 'You were with us, too.' Ridiculous, tender palms, vulnerable fingers for a man to have. 'Don't worry yourself.' That made the final push, broke the whole pain down on her. 'If you do, you'll worry us.'

Mary swayed with the ache of losing them – the two most elegant, good and dependable gentlemen she knew. The Uncles looked on, stuttered into a clasp of hands. The fridge hummed and ticked.

Then Morgan said, for both of them, 'We do love you.' A kindness which mauled through her, making her almost unwilling to listen when he added, 'You have to go, though. We all know.'

'Don't be sad for us. We don't require it.' Bryn swung up and round the table to hug her so powerfully that the pressure made her breathless as well as glad. She wanted to shrink, to regress and be a small person again in his arms, to slip back with him to a place without decisions or change.

He kissed her forehead, light and neat. 'How are you now?'

'Good. Good enough.' Her words were still frail, and also low, to make them privately his. 'Is that a new sweater?'

'Well. It is, yes. We opened our Christmas presents to each other. Cheer us up.'

She hugged him quickly, to ease out the turn in her stomach. 'Now . . . You'll start me crying again.'

Morgan chipped in, 'And my cardigan – that's new as well. Thanks for noticing. Funny colour. Bryn's never been good at colours. Have you, Bryn?'

Which eased the atmosphere enough to let Bryn squeeze Mary's shoulder and trot back to his seat. They all relaxed by a few degrees and tried to be simply a family having breakfast and chatting.

And, of course, they did have to talk about her trip. They ran over the route of her journey again, praised the many sandwiches Morgan had made, exchanged reassurances about her money and her spare money, telephoning, letters and all the ways they could think to keep near to each other while they were apart.

When it was time, Mary left the house and climbed Charter Road unburdened. Bryn had shouldered her rucksack before she could stop him and gravely threatened to fight her if she tried to take charge of her holdall. Morgan contented himself with the carrier bag of sandwiches and bottled water.

They processed along flat-fronted streets of houses busy with the signs of redundancy payouts and heavy, pointless time. Woodwork had been painted and repainted, windows and doors replaced, stone cladding and satellite dishes installed. The video shop, the off-licence, the bookie's and the post office, the late-night shop, were all defended with roll-down shutters and grilles. They were living through nervous days.

Under the additions and improvements, the lean, low rows of houses stayed much the same: accommodation built to hold the workers required by a long-failed copper deposit and a web of narrow coal seams, now worked out. Planted without warning in a steep, damp cul-de-sac of green, the town had become accustomed to a rising scale of abandonments.

At the bus stop, Bryn dropped Mary's holdall and twisted out from under her rucksack, inhaling and stretching one arm with relief. Morgan leaned his back against the wall, life whistling between grey lips. 'Duw, you need a bus to *get* to the bus, don't you?'

Bryn shook Mary's hand, darting in with the movement and making a hollowness clamber in her arms.

from everything you need **265**

'You're not going?'

'No. Just shaking your hand.' He touched his fingertips to her hair and briefly tensed his mouth. '*Ille terrarum nihil praeter omnes angulus ridet.* Don't know that one, do you? *That little corner beyond all the world is full of smiles for me.* You're my corner. Always.' He nodded, placidly, agreeing unrepentantly that he was being sentimental. 'You'll knock 'em dead, you know. They won't ever have seen a Mary Lamb. *Hoc vince.*'

'By this, conquer.'

'That's right.'

And the Uncles waited until Mary's bus came, kissed her in a rush, helped with the luggage, gave her peppermints for the journey, a touch more cash, and then waved and waved and waved her a good goodbye.

After she was gone they had tea in Ianetta's, feeling oddly exposed with only themselves there and no one in between. They linked arms gently going down the hill, taking it slow.

Although it was barely midday when they got home, they drew their curtains and went to bed. They then made quick, despairing love in the manner of the recently bereaved. Morgan used his inhaler. They both slept.

looking at you: for the tron bar and george

JANICE GALLOWAY
JANICE GALLOWAY

There's glitter as they walk around behind there, black T-shirts making the bottles come and go. Through a burr of other people's talk, the soft clash of glasses, Nick's at the end of the counter, slivering slices of citrus so thin you can see through them from here. Sheer circles. There's enough for 20 on the board and he's going for one more, the little yellow tit of the end of lemon still cupped inside his palm. He lifts them like cards when he's done, a suit and a half in one hand, drops the lot into a water jug, jumps back when the splash comes. It gets him anyway. He looks over at Marc in case Marc's seen and winks, whirling the jug like a brandy bowl, swaying his hips like a stripper. He pours himself a glass and drinks dancing, his pinkie and fourth finger cocked. Naked. All his fingers are naked. Rod comes, a tray of half-pints in both fists. He slides behind Nick to halfway then stops, shifting the tray to the one hand like a barbell, whispering. His double earring rubs against itself when he whispers, secret barman stuff, almost kissing Nick's neck. Rod's got baby-girl lips, pale and sheeny. They both have the same short hairstyle, neck like mushroom stalks, translucent under the bar lights. They don't need to exchange looks, just smile looking in the same direction, crotch to arse as Nick goes on slicing, listening, his nape bared. Rod flips the tray higher when Marc comes over too; it's right up on the balls of his fingertips. Now there's room for three. Whatever it is he says they all laugh and you've never seen so many perfect teeth. All those creamy ivories. The open mouths attract Steven, ten tan fingers dripping from glasses he's just washed, so he has to hold them up like a flamenco dancer to save the others from splashes. Little rivulets of water snake down his arms, veins coursing on the surface. Nick looks thin as a stick beside him, all angles and pipecleaner bends soft to the touch you bet you bet. Steve is square and olive-skinned, early Elvis sideburns with a fine silver chain tipping his breastbone. A stiff chest, a heartbeat you'd be able to hear out loud, feel if he stood close. He's the most beautiful man you ever saw and he only has eyes for Marc. Marc knows and doesn't mind. Not at all. Marc's straight as a cucumber, so white he's blue. Celtic. Opening his shirt would make you snow blind. Temporarily. His nipples would be like bites. He has red, red, coxcomb hair. And he's not looking at the barmaid. Nobody's looking at the barmaid. He's looking at you.

mrs darwin

CAROL ANN DUFFY

7 April 1852.
Went to the Zoo.
I said to Him –
Something about that Chimpanzee over there reminds me of you.

about the authors

Keith Adamson is an architect. He has had many stories published in magazines and anthologies including 'Just Another Sunday' from *Oranges and Lemons*.

Sebastian Beaumont was a sometime model and is now a taxi driver. He is the author of several novels, among them *Heroes are Hard to Find*, *Two* and *On the Edge*, now in its second edition.

Toni Davidson's first novel *Scar Culture* has been published in nine languages. He has edited two anthologies – *And Thus Will I Freely Sing* and *Intoxication*. He is currently working on a play and a second novel.

Jack Dickson has had several trial runs at a variety of careers, including fashion designer, model, bass player, bouncer and boxer. He now writes gay pornography to put bread on the table and crime fiction to feed his soul. His novels include *Oddfellows*, *Crossing Jordan* and the Jas Anderson mysteries *Free Form* and *Banged Up*. His short fiction has been published widely in the US. At present he is working on a number of cinematic treatments for Monkey Films Ltd. His latest porn effort, *Still Waters*, was published in summer 2001. The third Jas Anderson mystery, *Some Kind of Love*, hits the shelves at the end of 2001. Jack lives in Glasgow with his man and his dog.

Bill Douglas is best known for the trilogy of films which he wrote and directed: *My Childhood*, *My Ain Folk* and *My Way Home*. His only other full-length feature film was *Comrades*. He also produced a 15-minute student film – *Come Dancing* – which is about a homosexual encounter and has rarely been screened. He died of cancer in 1991.

Carol Anne Duffy was born in Glasgow and attended university in Liverpool before moving to London. She has won many awards, including a Scottish Arts Council Book Award for her collections *Standing Female Nude* and *The Other Country*. She was awarded a Somerset Maugham Award in 1988 for her collection *Selling Manhattan*, The Dylan Thomas Award in 1989 and a Cholmondeley award in 1992. *Mean Time* won the 1993 Whitbread Award for poetry and the Forward Prize. Her *Selected Poems* are published by Penguin and her poems for children by Faber.

Martin Foreman was born in Dundee and grew up in Edinburgh. He has lived in London, Los Angeles, New York and Rio de Janeiro, but returns to his roots at least twice a year. He is the author of several works of fiction and non-fiction, most recently the novel *The Butterfly's Wing* and the study *AIDS and Men*. Samples of his work can be seen on www.martinforeman.com.

Ellen Galford has had several novels published, among them *The Fires of the Bride, Mol Cutpurse: Her True Story, Queendom Come* and *The Dyke and The Dybbuk*. She lives in Edinburgh.

Janice Galloway's first book, *The Trick is to Keep Breathing*, won the MIND/Allen Lane Book of the Year and was shortlisted for the Whitbread First Novel Award. *Foreign Parts* won the McVitie's Prize. She has also published two short story collections, *Blood* and *Where You Find It*. She is currently completing a third novel.

Alasdair Gray has published many works of brilliance, among them *Lanark, 1982, Janine, Something Leather* and *Poor Things*. He has also published the polemic *Why Scots Should Rule Scotland*. His latest book is an anthology of prefaces.

Sue Green was born in Lancashire and has lived in Scotland for 23 years. She has had short stories published in *New Writing Scotland*, *West Coast Magazine*, *Deliberately Thirsty* and *Nerve* and is currently working on a collection of short stories and her first novel.

Thomas Healy has published two novels, *It Might Have Been Jerusalem* and *Rolling*. *A Hurting Business*, his memoir as a lifelong boxing fan, was published in 1996. He was born in Glasgow and still lives there.

Jackie Kay was born in Edinburgh and grew up in Glasgow. She has published two collections of poetry, the first of which, *The Adoption Papers* (Bloodaxe 1991), won the Saltire and Forward Prizes. The second, *Other Lovers* (Bloodaxe 1993), won a Somerset Maugham Award. *Trumpet* is her first novel. She is currently working on another novel and a collection of short stories. She lives in Manchester.

James Kelman's *How Late It Was, How Late* won the Booker Prize in 1994. Apart from his works of fiction, including *A Dissatisfaction* and *The Good Times*, he has also published *Some Recent Attacks: Essays Cultural and Political*. His most recently published work is *Translated Accounts, A Novel*.

A.L. Kennedy has published three collections of stories and several novels, the latest being *Everything You Need*.

Gordon Legge has had two novels and two volumes of short stories published, the latest being *Near Neighbours*. His first novel, *The Shoe*, was shortlisted for the Saltire First Book of the Year award. He has appeared in many anthologies, among them *Children of Albion Rovers*. He won this year's Robert Louis Stevenson award.

Jimmy McGovern has many screen-writing credits, among them *Priest, Cracker, The Lakes*. Amazingly, he's not Scottish.

Joseph Mills has had published one novel, *Towards the End*, and one novella and collection of short stories, *Obsessions*. Many short stories have been published in anthologies, the latest being *The Picador Book of Contemporary Scottish Fiction* and *New Writing Scotland 17*. Joseph divides his valuable creative writing time between an imaginary penthouse flat in Manhattan overlooking Central Park and a dingy high rise flat in The Gorbals overlooking The Gorbals. As well as a fantasy occupation as personal shower assistant to Michael Owen he also works for Glasgow City Libraries, where he enthusiastically promotes Culture Leisure and Homosexuality.

Edwin Morgan has published many works, including *From the Video Box* and *Virtual and Other Realities*. His *Collected Poems* was published in 1990. He was born in 1920 and lives in Glasgow.

Dilys Rose has published two collections of poems, three of short stories – most recently *War Dolls* – and a novel, *Pest Maiden*. She is currently working on new poetry and short stories and a second novel. She lives in Edinburgh.

Manda Scott was born and raised in a small village south of the river (Clyde). She studied veterinary medicine at Glasgow University before the promise of fast horses and astonishing women lured her south. Since then, veterinary medicine has given way to writing as a career although, unaccountably, she has not yet found her way home. *Stronger Than Death* is the third novel in the Kellen Stewart series, the first novel of which, *Hen's Teeth*, was shortlisted for the Orange Prize for Women's Fiction. Her latest novel, *No Good Deed*, marks the start of a new series.

Ali Smith has published poetry, two short story collections – *Free Love and Other Stories* and *Other Stories and Other Stories* – and two novels, *Like* and *Hotel World*, in addition to having several plays produced in London and at the Edinburgh Fringe.

Alexander Trocchi's *Cain's Book* was banned in Britain in 1963. He is also the author of, among other works, *Young Adam* and *Helen and Desire*.

Irvine Welsh you all know. All the Mr Joneses hated him when he first appeared but tried to say something good because he was new and hot and they didn't want to give away their complete and utter nothingness. Now that he has produced many great novels, stories, plays and films, they will feel free to savage his latest book, *Glue*. (By the way, the editor, not the author, wrote this.)

Christopher Whyte was born in Glasgow in 1952. He took a degree at Cambridge before going to teach English in Italy, where he stayed until 1985. Since returning to Scotland he has published a prize-winning book of Gaelic poems *Uirsgeul/Myth* (Gairm 1991), the anthology *An Aghaidh na Siorraifheachd: Ochdnar Bhard Gaidhlig: In the Face of Eternity: Eight Gaelic poets* (Polygon 1991) and four novels in English: *Euphemia MacFarrigle and the Laughing Virgin* (1995), *The Warlock of Strathearn* (1997), *The Gay Decameron* (1998) and *The Cloud Machinery* (2000). His poetry has been translated into Italian, Catalan, Croatian and Albanian, and his fiction into both Italian and German.

Graeme Woolaston had three novels published between 1985 and 1995. For most of the 1990s he combined this with work as an arts administrator, but now concentrates on freelance writing. He lives near Glasgow.